50 PROJECTS
RELAYS, SCRs
AND TRIACs

ALSO BY THE SAME AUTHOR

No. BP30 Two Transistor Electronic Projects
No. BP32 How to Build Your Own Metal and Treasure Locators
No. BP35 Handbook of IC Audio Preamplifier and Power Amplifier Construction
No. BP39 50 (FET) Field Effective Transistor Projects
No. BP43 How to Make Walkie-Talkies
No. BP48 Electronic Projects for Beginners
No. BP57 How to Build Your Own Solid State Oscilloscope
No. BP67 Counter Driver and Numeral Display Projects

50 PROJECTS USING
RELAYS, SCRs
AND TRIACs

by

F.G. RAYER, T.Eng.(CEI), Assoc.IERE

BABANI PRESS
The Publishing Division of
Babani Trading and Finance Co. Ltd.
The Grampians
Shepherds Bush Road
London W6 7NF
England

Although every care is taken with the preparation of this book, the publishers or author will not be responsible in any way for any errors that might occur.

© 1977 BABANI PRESS

I.S.B.N. 0 85934 040 6

First Published — March 1977
Reprinted — October 1979

Printed and Manufactured in Great Britain by
C. Nicholls & Co. Ltd.

CONTENTS

Page

RELAYS
Relay Operation 8
Coil Voltage and Current 9
Contacts 11
Hold-On Circuit 11
Delayed Circuit. 13
Back EMF Suppression. 13
Power Increase 14
Avoiding Current or Voltage 15
Relay Testing 15
Other Relays 16
Multi-Circuit Switching. 17
Relay Supplies 18
Relay Timer 19
Relay Priority Indicator 21
Motor Reversing 21
The Steady Hand. 24
Automatic Train Control 25
Automatic Emergency Light 27
Bell Substitute for Deaf 28
UJT Delay 29
Direct Relay Light Control .30

SCRs
Silicon Controlled Rectifiers 31
SCR Test 33
SCR Types. 35
Characteristics 36
Buzzer Substitute 37
Mains Supply 39
Burglar Alarm. 41
Broken Circuit Alarm. 43
Rain Alarm 45
Audio Oscillator 47
Zener Triggered Oscillator. .48
Sound Operated Switch 50
6V Touchswitch 53
Adjustable Grip Tester 53
Silent "Steady Hand". 55

OFF Switching SCRs 56
SCR Flasher 57
Train and Model Control 58
Control by Light 61
Sensitive Light Operated Switch 64
Mains Light Operated Circuit 65
Audio Light Modulator 67
Multi-Channel 71
Delayed Circuits 71
UJT Delay On or Delay Off 74
1 to 5 Minute Timer 76
Priority Indicator 79
Sequence Control 80
Wiper Delay 81
Vehicle Protector 84
Automatic Battery Charger 88
Excess Voltage Breaker 90
Dimmer/Heat Control 91
Safety 93
Full-Wave Dimmer 95
Radio Interference 97

TRIACs
Drill or Motor Controller 98
3-Position Control 100
Low Voltage AC Motor Control 100
Temperature Warning 101

INTRODUCTION

Relays, silicon controlled rectifiers (SCRs) and bi-directional triodes (TRIACs) may be employed in a wide range of circuits. These extend over the whole field of motor control, dimming and heat control, delayed, timing and light-sensitive circuits, and include warning devices, various novelties, light modulators, priority indicators, excess voltage breakers, and numerous other devices.

The purpose of this book is to give tried, practical working circuits which should present the minimum of difficulty. Relays, SCRs and TRIACs do in fact have a wide practical utility in electronics today.

In most circuits there is a wide latitude in component values and types, allowing easy modification of circuits, or ready adaptation of them to individual needs.

RELAYS

Though many switching applications originally performed by relays are now carried out by semiconductor devices such as transistors and thyristors, the relay still has many uses. Among its particular advantages are the complete electrical isolation it offers between the operating or coil circuit on the one hand, and the contact or switched circuit on the other hand, and the fact that it can readily control more than one circuit.

As a relay is a rugged, easily understood and easily used item, it is often found in circuits which could employ a semiconductor device instead, as well as in those circuits where there is virtually no substitute for it. Relays are available for a wide range of operating voltages and currents, and in types which allow them to switch mains circuits, or aerial circuits in transmitting-receiving equipment, as well as perform numerous other switching functions.

Relay Operation

A relay is a magnetically operated switch, and the way in which one popular type operates will be clear from Figure 1. The turns of the operating coil are contained in a bobbin, which has a central core. The armature is pivoted on a sharp edge, where it is kept in place by a light spring and screw.

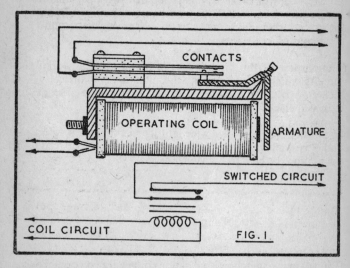

The contacts shown are normally open, but when the coil is energised magnetic force pulls the armature to the core. An insulated push rod on the other end of the armature moves one contact, so that the circuit is completed. When current ceases to flow through the coil, the armature is released and the contacts open. The coil may be wound for any normal voltage, and the contacts may if wished be suitable for the switching of mains voltages.

Figure 2 shows some more relays, and there will generally be a number of contacts. The 2-way relay operates in the same manner as a 2-way switch. The circuit is normally from A to B, but when the coil is energised, the circuit is from A to C.

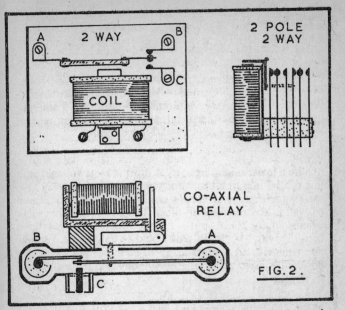

FIG. 2.

The 2-pole 2-way relay has two separate sets of contacts, each of change-over type, and operated by an insulated push rod. In some circuit applications, four or more poles are required, and relays are available with several isolated sets of contacts.

The co-axial relay is a type primarily intended for switching the aerial circuit of high frequency equipment, as from reception to transmission. Here, co-axial socket A is normally switched to B, but when the relay operates the push rod moves the contact and transfers the circuit to the co-axial outlet C.

Relays are made in a great variety of types, from large, mains-voltage devices to miniature, lightweight relays intended for model aircraft and similar purposes.

Coil Voltage and Current

Typical coil operating voltages are 6V, 12V, 24V and 230/250V AC. This is the voltage for normal working, but most relays will prove to be satisfactory with a fairly substantial reduction in coil voltage. However, if the voltage is too low, the relay does not operate strongly enough, or refuses to work at all.

If necessary, the current required by the coil can be found from Ohm's Law. Current = Voltage/Relay Resistance. So a 6V 100 ohm relay will require 6/100 = 0.06 ampere, or 60mA. On the other hand, a 6 volt 2,000 ohm relay would only require 6/2,000 = 0.003A or 3mA.

It will be seen that relays with high resistance coils will require a lower operating current, for the same voltage, and this can be important in some circuits. Where a relay is working with a lower voltage than normal, the coil current will fall in accordance with this. Thus a 12V 600 ohm relay would require 20mA, but if it were found to work satisfactorily with 9V, the current would be only 15mA. A low operating current is most likely to be important in battery powered equipment, as lengthy working is then possible with small cells.

Small, lightweight relays may have a coil resistance of several thousand ohms, and operate with a very low current. They are particularly suitable for models. For normal use where weight is not important, a 6V relay will usually be from about 100 to 200 ohms, while a 12V relay can be about 400 to 800 ohms. A typical 24V relay can have a 570 ohm coil, and a 230V AC relay a 7,300 ohm coil.

With some relays, the spacing between armature and core may be adjustable, and also the return spring tension. Careful changes here may allow a relay to be made more sensitive, if needed.

The "holding down" current of a relay is lower than that which is required to operate it initially, and can be altered by adjusting the return spring tension.

With surplus relays of unknown resistance, the coil can be measured with a meter. This will show what current the winding will require with any particular voltage. A suitable coil voltage is easily found by trial, and is the lowest figure which will give strong, reliable operation.

Relays intended for AC will have laminated cores. When using an ordinary relay from AC, a check should be made that it does not grow hot. Low voltage relays may often be run satisfactorily from AC, but this depends on the length of time the winding is energised, as well as other factors.

Contacts

Small, low voltage relays such as are used in models often have contacts only suitable for low power. Maximum current may be 1 ampere or lower, at up to 24V. This means the relay is only suitable for light work, such as switching small actuators or motors, and for similar purposes.

Large relays can switch several amperes at mains voltage if necessary. Where large power is to be controlled, reference should be made to the manufacturer's data.

If a small relay, intended for low current and voltage, is used to switch high voltages or currents, its contacts are likely to fail rapidly. They will become blackened, or weld together and refuse to open, so should not be used outside their ratings.

Hold-On Circuit

It is sometimes necessary that a relay circuit, when once operated, should remain on until manually re-set. An example of this is in a warning circuit where the warning may be from a contact mat. Here, only brief contact may be obtained as the contact surfaces close, but a warning bell would be required to ring continuously once the circuit has been operated. Similar needs may arise with light or sound-operated circuits, and other equipment.

Hold-on in this way may readily be provided by using one set of relay contacts, as at A in Figure 3. Here, the relay coil is energised by current from the transistor, so that the circuit to R1 is completed. Switch S1 is normally closed. Once the relay has closed current flows through S1 and R1 to its coil, so that it remains in this state. The relay can only be opened by pressing S1, so as to interrupt the circuit to the coil.

11

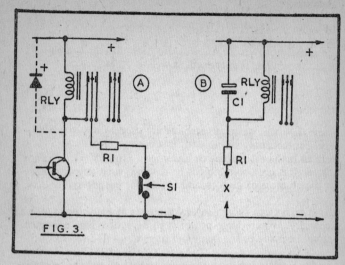

FIG. 3.

R1 is chosen to provide a suitable holding-on current. As example, if the relay needs some 15–20mA to hold on, and a 9V supply is used, then R1 plus the coil resistance can be 470 ohms.

The second set of contacts is used to switch on the warning lamp, bell, or other controlled device.

A circuit of this kind can also be used to obtain a more positive operation of the relay, when current provided for the coil from the coil controlling circuit is liable to be interrupted or fluctuating, so that the relay tends to vibrate or operate intermittently. In this case, the steady current through R1 will hold the relay firmly closed until S1 is operated. In some circuits of this kind it is possible to dispense with S1, increasing the value of R1 so that it provides a steady bias current for the coil, which is in itself insufficient to operate the relay or hold it closed. Less current is then required from the transistor or other control circuit.

Delayed Circuit

In some circumstances it may be necessary to delay the working of the relay, so that it is not operated by a brief supply of current, but only closes when current is maintained for an interval. The circuit at B is suitable for this purpose.

The relay coil is operated by closing of the circuit at X. Current flows through R1, but can only operate the relay when the capacitor C1 has charged up to the required potential. Momentarily closing the circuit X will thus not operate the relay at all.
The time constant of the circuit will depend on the capacitor value, and resistance of the relay coil and R1. It is necessary that when the circuit X is permanently completed, the relay receives sufficient voltage to operate. This sets a limit on the value of R1. To increase the delay, C1 can be of higher value, with R1 as high as practical. With a 500 ohm relay operated from a 15V supply, a delay of about 2 seconds would be expected with 1.5k for R1 and 3500μF for C1. Exact results will depend on the voltage needed to close the relay. The circuit at A may be added, if wished, so that when the relay commences to operate, current through R1 in A also becomes available for the coil, closing the contacts smartly.

The circuit at B is not very feasible unless the relay coil is of fairly high resistance, as otherwise extremely large values are needed for C1. A high resistance, low current relay is most suitable, if a delay of more than a second or so is wanted.

Back EMF Suppression

The relay is a magnetic device in which energy is stored in the field surrounding the coil. When current to the coil is interrupted, the magnetic field collapses, and produces a back emf, or voltage. This can be of importance in some circuits, and especially in those controlled by semiconductor devices.

With a low operating voltage, and transistor or other semiconductor able to withstand the small back emf generated, no breakdown is likely from this cause. The back emf is also much reduced when there is not an immediate interruption of coil current, but rather a slow fall from working current.

Where the back emf may damage associated items, it can be suppressed by connecting a diode across the relay winding. This diode conducts when the reversed emf appears, so suppressing it. A capacitor, or resistor-capacitor circuit is also sometimes used, as the capacitor tends to absorb the back emf. Values may not be very critical, though this depends on the relay and other factors. The polarity for a diode is shown at A, Figure 3. Diodes such as the 1N4001 (50V 1A) will generally be convenient.

Power Increase

A relay could be looked upon as a device able to step-up power — a relatively low voltage, low current input to the coil is able to control a higher voltage, larger current circuit. Despite this, a circuit where there is only a small change of current, at low voltage, could not operate a relay directly when the latter has to switch large power. This can be overcome by using two relays, as in Figure 4. Here, relay 1 is of sensitive type, and its contacts are only required to handle the voltage and current necessary for relay 2, which can switch in turn a circuit handling over 1,000 watts.

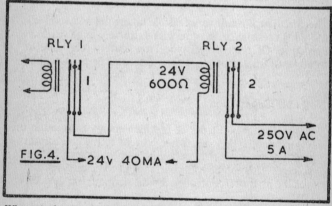

Where inductive loads are switched, a diode can be connected across the inductive load, as already described, to suppress the back emf. Such a diode would be across the 600 ohm coil, and it would greatly reduce sparking at the contacts of relay 1, thus lengthening their life.

Avoiding Current or Voltage

A relay is often used to relieve the control circuit of the need to carry a high current, or have a high voltage present. This allows a high current motor (e.g., vehicle self-starter) or other powerful item to be switched on by a suitable relay which is near to it, so as to avoid voltage drop in long connections. The relay coil only needs a much smaller current, so leads to it can be of any reasonable length.

A similar arrangement may occasionally be convenient when a bell is to be operated by a very long circuit, which has so much resistance that it is not possible to supply the appropriate bell or chime directly from it. In this case, the push and extended circuit only need to complete the path to the relay coil. Closure of the relay contacts can then provide whatever current or voltage may be necessary.

A relay is sometimes used for keying a transmitter which is of other than low power, or which requires to be keyed in a high voltage circuit. Here, the key interrupts the coil current, and the relay contacts control the high voltage. By this means, no dangerous voltages are present at the Morse key itself.

Relay Testing

If necessary, the relay coil can be tested with a meter. This will also show the coil resistance, if not known. A faulty coil is unusual, though may be found with old or surplus relays. Rewinding to repair a broken coil is not difficult with some types having few turns, but is awkward with high-resistance coils doped with insulating varnish.

Contacts can be checked for zero resistance when closed, but may need cleaning or adjusting on old relays. The operating mechanism is generally straightforward and unlikely to cause trouble.

Other Relays

Various other relays and electro-magnetic devices are seen, and have particular uses. Relays may be operated by solenoids with sliding plungers. Reed relays have a contact assembly inserted in the operating coil. Mains relays for some types of equipment may consist of shaped tubes containing mercury, which completes circuits when the tubes are tilted by an electro-magnetic mechanism. Polarised relays incorporate a permanent magnet, while magnetically operated step switches transfer circuits in sequence.

A vehicle charging circuit cut-out is a type of relay which closes when the generator is producing power, but opens to disconnect the battery when the generator is not delivering current. Leakage trips and circuit breakers are types of magnetically released switches, in which a leakage current, unbalanced current, or excess current triggers the mechanism, so that contacts spring open to break the circuit.

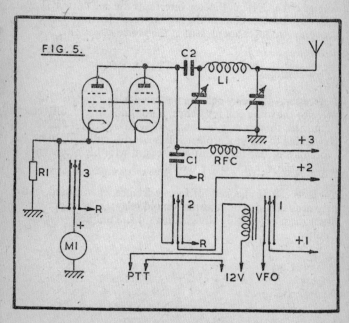

Multi-Circuit Switching

A relay having several sets of contacts can switch numerous circuits simultaneously, and this is of great utility in some equipment. Figure 5 shows a relay being used for transceiver switching — that is, the changing over from reception to transmission with a combined transmitter-receiver. This will also give a good idea of how other circuits can be arranged, so that several are all controlled together by a relay, and thus by a simple manual switch, or similar device.

When the press-to-talk switch PTT is closed, the relay is energised from the 12V supply. Contacts 1 take the regulated high tension supply 1 to the variable frequency oscillator of the transmitter (this controls working frequency). Contacts 2 connect the high tension 2 point to the screen grids of the two power amplifier valves, so that they operate to supply power to the aerial. L1 is the power amplifier tank coil, tuned by the variable capacitors shown. Relay contacts 3 transfer meter M1 to the cathode circuit, to indicate cathode current, resistor R1 being a shunt of low value.

With such circuits, the highest potential supply 3 is generally left on the power amplifier anodes, which are controlled by the removal of the screen grid voltage by section 2 of the relay.

When the PTT switch is released, the VFO is switched off, HT2 is switched to R to operate certain receiver circuits, and the set of contacts 3 transfer the meter to the receiver circuit, so that it can act as a tuning and signal strength meter. Radio frequency signals are taken to the receiver through the small isolating capacitor C1. C2 is to keep high tension voltages from the aerial circuit.

The push-to-talk switch will normally be incorporated on the microphone, so that rapid change-over from transmit to receive is obtained easily. If necessary, further sets of contacts can be present, to control other circuits. With some equipment, part of the output of the microphone is made to operate the relay. If so, transmission is automatically obtained when the user speaks.

It will be seen that it is easy to control numerous circuits, entirely separate from each other if necessary, and all at different potentials.

Relays for purposes such as this, and for commercial equipment, are often of plug-in type. These fit an eight-socket or other suitable holder, so that they can be removed or replaced without any disturbance to permanent circuits.

Relay Supplies

In many circuits, the same battery or other supply used to operate other circuits will energise the relay coil. With mains operated equipment, a suitable supply can be obtained from a low voltage transformer, with rectifier and smoothing capacitor. This can provide 6V, 12V, or whatever voltage the relay requires.

Where a DC supply of this kind is available, but of too high a voltage, it is often feasible to place a resistor in series with the relay coil. Its value is easily found from Ohm's Law. As example, assume a 12V relay taking 50mA is to be operated from a supply providing 18V. Voltage to be dropped = 18 − 12 = 6V. The required series resistor is V/I or 6/0.05 = 120 ohm.

With mains operated equipment, the current taken by the relay coil is usually quite unimportant. But with battery equipment, it is wise to use a relay having a high coil resistance. The current taken by its coil is then relatively low, so that batteries of normal size can have a reasonably long life, even if the relay remains energised for some time.

In later circuits, current for the relay coil will be seen taken from battery and mains circuits, and methods such as those shown can generally be adopted without difficulty for any relay circuit.

Relay Timer

The circuit in Figure 6 gives an adjustable time interval of 1 to 30 seconds, and can be used for repetitive processes such as photo enlarging, or for setting a time limit to the completion of simple electronic puzzles, or similar purposes.

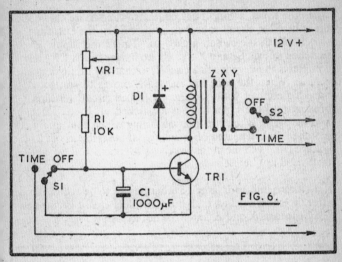

FIG. 6.

By using a 2-pole switch for S1/S2, the circuit is completely switched off and capacitor C1 is fully discharged, thus giving reliable repetition of the interval chosen. When the switch is moved to "Time" no collector current flows, because the base of TR1 is negative due to capacitor C1. C1 commences to charge through R1 and VR1, and when the charge has reached a sufficient level TR1 conducts, as its base has moved positive. Collector current closes the relay.

If VR1 is 250k, this gives an interval of about 30 seconds, and the interval grows shorter as the resistance in circuit is reduced. The interval can be increased by using a larger value for C1, or reduced by using smaller values. C1 should not be a poor component with a high leakage current, or the circuit may fail to operate at all, especially with high values for VR1.

The diode is to suppress back emf. With a 2000 ohm relay the "on" current will be about 6mA, so a small battery supply is suitable. A relay with a lower resistance coil may be used, but this will increase the current taken from the battery. However, many other transistor types and values may be used successfully.

When the timer is "off" relay contacts X and Y are closed, but the controlled circuit is broken by pole S2 of the Off/Time switch. With the switch moved to "Time" the supply is switched on, via S2 and X—Y. S1 no longer shorts C1, and completes the negative line circuit, so that the timing sequence begins. When the time has elapsed X moves to contact Z, breaking contact with Y. The controlled circuit remains broken until the timer has been switched off by S1/S2 and also on again, when the interval during which the supply is switched on is repeated. For enlarger timing, the use of a low voltage lamp will mean that a relay with mains voltage contacts need not be used.

If a buzzer, indicator lamp or other item is to be switched on after the chosen delay, then the controlled circuit is wired to relay contacts X and Z, and S2 is not necessary.

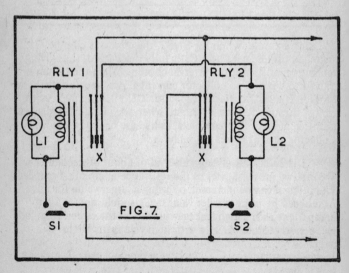

FIG.7.

Relay Priority Indicator

This may be used for games of "Snap" or will show which was the first person or team ready to reply in quiz games. There are two push-button switches, S1 and S2, for the players or teams, and additional switches can be connected in parallel, for team use. Each player has his own indicator lamp, L1 or L2, Figure 7.

The contacts X of each relay are normally closed. Should button S1 be pressed first, current flows through L1 and the relay coil, and through contacts X of relay 2. As relay 1 is energised, contacts X of relay 1 are open. This interrupts the circuit to relay 2, so that closing switch S2 has no result. If push-switch S2 is closed first, L2 lights instead, and contacts X of relay 2 open, so that operating switch S1 has no effect. In this way, the person who operates his switch first captures the circuit, and only his lamp will light. The effect is almost instantaneous, clearly showing who had priority. (If an even faster circuit response is wanted, it can be obtained electronically as shown later.)

The relays and lamps can be chosen to suit the operating voltage and 6V relays, with 6.3V 0.15A or similar bulbs, can be used. As an alternative, 6V 40 ohm or similar relays could be used in series with 6.3V 0.15A bulbs, if a 12V supply were to be employed. Other working voltages would of course be equally suitable.

It is convenient to have the relays and indicator lamps in a case, with flexible leads to S1 and S2, so that the latter are easily within reach of the competitors.

With operation at low voltage, there is of course no danger even if leads, bell-pushes, or other parts are not completely insulated.

Motor Reversing

Relays are frequently used to reverse motors, especially in radio controlled models, and may also be used for this purpose in train layouts, and elsewhere. The way in which the relay is connected will depend on the type of motor, and sometimes on the supply.

Many small model motors have a permanent magnet field, and will run from direct current only. The DC supply can be from an accumulator, dry batteries, or mains unit with rectifier. If the polarity of the supply to the motor is reversed, so is the direction of rotation of the motor.

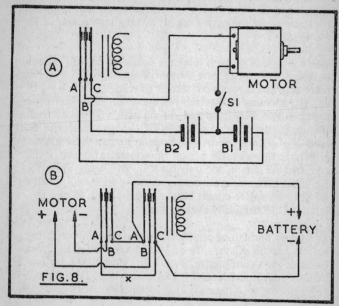

FIG. 8.

Figure 8A shows a method of reversing this type of motor, with only a single pole change-over relay. When the relay contacts provide a circuit from A to B, battery B1 is in use. When the circuit is instead from B to C, the second battery B2 operates the motor. The batteries B1 and B2 are connected so as to supply opposite polarity to the motor, to reverse it. This method can be convenient for a model boat, where a lower voltage, or used battery can provide the current for motion astern, at reduced speed. Otherwise B1 and B2 will both be of the same voltage. Switch S1 (or a relay) is for switching off.

At B, another method of reversing the permanent magnet motor is shown, and this requires only a single battery. When the double-pole relay provides a circuit from A to B at each set of contacts, the polarity of the supply to the motor is as

22

shown. This can be for forward running of the model. When the relay is energised, the contacts provide circuits from B to C in each case, and the supply to the motor is reversed. Should reduced speed be required in one direction only, a variable resistor may be inserted at X. This can be of advantage for motion astern with a model boat.

Motors which are intended to run from alternating current as well as direct current, and some of the larger model motors for accumulators, have a wound field, instead of the permanent magnet. These run in the same direction, whatever the polarity of the supply. They cannot be reversed by the circuit shown for the permanent magnet motors. In order to reverse them, it is necessary to change over the polarity of the supply to the field, or to the armature (but not both).

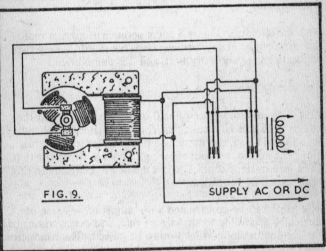

FIG. 9.   SUPPLY AC OR DC

Figure 9 shows a circuit for this purpose. Some motors will have separate brush and field connections available, so that they can be connected to give rotation in either direction. With other motors, it will be necessary to locate the wires which come from the brushes or field coil, and to separate these, so that they can be extended to run to the relay.

The relay contacts are wired to reverse the supply to the brushes and armature. However, if it is more convenient, the

23

leads to the field coil can be reversed by the relay instead.

In the circuit shown, the armature windings and field coil are in parallel. A motor may instead have the armature and field in series. This will not effect the method of wiring the relay to produce reverse polarity to brushes or field, but the parallel or series connections should be retained, as the case may be, if the motor is to run correctly from the same voltage as before.

The motor may be operated from DC (batteries, or mains unit with rectifier) or from AC (low-voltage transformer). This will have no effect on the reversing obtained.

It is convenient to have the relay near the motor it controls. This is easy with some models, but impracticable or awkward with others.

With the circuits in Figure 8 and a permanent magnet motor, the relay can be at any distance from the motor as only two connections are necessary to it, and it is unmodified.

The Steady Hand

This is an amusing game of skill quite often seen, and the circuit in Figure 10 is suitable. The competitor has a handle on a flexible lead, and carrying a ring. He has to move this along the course, without allowing contact between the two. Even intermittent contact causes the bell to continue to ring until switch S1 is opened.

The game can be constructed with almost any degree of difficulty according to the size of ring, and convolutions of the conductor along which it must be moved. The conductor can be a copper or brass tube or rod, or a stout, rigid wire. It is convenient to have it supported at both ends by wooden members, and to have sleeving or similar insulation for a short distance each end, so that the ring can rest there without completing the circuit. About 2 feet or 0.5m of conductor, bent so as to provide corners and curves of various kinds, will be suitable. If the game is not to be too difficult, the ring ought to be of such a diameter that there is at least ¼ inch (5 to 6mm) of free space between it and the conductor.

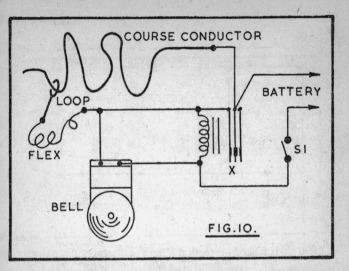

FIG.10.

Relay contacts X are normally open, and there is no contact between loop and conductor. If contact arises, the relay is operated so that contacts X close, permanently completing and locking-on the circuit until S1 is opened.

It is convenient to have relay, bell and battery in a box which can form the base of the whole game. Vertical strips will support the course conductor, and one end of this and the handle are wired as shown.

Automatic Train Control

Various automatic sequential operations can be arranged with the aid of relays, and the circuit for two trains, in Figure 11, will show one method of arranging these.

The whole track is a continuous circuit, which may of course include points and other sections of rail, in the usual way. Sections A and D receive power directly. Section B is isolated and receives power through the relay coil, while section C is also isolated, but receives power only when the relay contacts X are closed. These contacts are normally open.

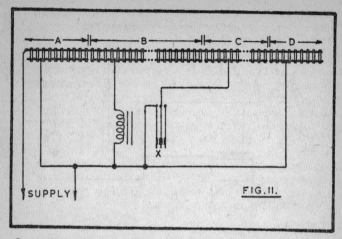

FIG. II.

SUPPLY

One train is placed on section C, and as contacts X are open, no power is available here. The other train is on the section of rail D—A, so is running normally to approach section B.

As soon as the second train leaves section A, power for it is obtained through the relay coil. This reduces speed of the second train, but contacts X close, so that full power is now available for the first train, resting on section C. This engine thus starts, and the train moves on to section D, to begin the track circuit.

The first train proceeds along section B, and on to section C, but as soon as no current is drawn by section B, the relay opens, and section C is isolated. The engine therefore stops here.

When the first train has completed the circuit and runs from section A on to section B, the train halted on section C moves away, and the whole procedure is repeated.

It is necessary that the relay coil is of sufficiently low resistance for the engine to continue to run, when on section B.

With most model trains, a relay of about 30 ohms will be suitable. With a 12V supply, about 6V will remain across the train motor, and about 6V will arise across the relay (assuming

26

current is 0.2 ampere). A 50 ohm relay was also found to work in this circuit, but a 47 ohm resistor was necessary in parallel with its coil, so that the combination was of sufficiently low resistance for the train not to halt when leaving section A. If a relay of sufficiently low resistance is not available, a surplus relay can be re-wound with stouter gauge wire, or it may be possible to devise a relay from a bell or buzzer electromagnet. Power must be so divided between the engine and the relay, that both operate reliably, when the train rests on part B of the track.

Similar switching arrangements may be used to operate signal lamps or other devices. Additional contacts on this relay could easily light red and green bulbs, suitably placed, to coincide with the motion of the trains.

Automatic Emergency Light

A strategically placed light which comes on automatically when a power cut arises can be very helpful for children or the infirm. It is possible to use a light-sensitive switch of the type described later for this purpose. Another approach is to have the emergency light so arranged that it is operated when the house mains fail to provide current. An arrangement of this kind could switch on full emergency lighting, but this would be costly, and not justified in the home. However, a single unit, placed to light stairway and landing, or in a bedroom, is readily provided.

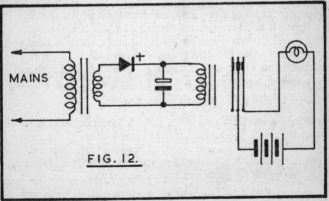

FIG. 12.

Figure 12 shows the circuit. Current from the house mains is taken to the transformer primary. The secondary with rectifier provides a low voltage to energise the relay, so that the contacts are normally open. The capacitor is generally necessary to avoid humming of the relay. When mains current fails, the relay is released, so the contacts close, switching on the battery operated lamp.

A small 5V bell transformer is suitable, and will consume negligible current when operating a 6V or similar relay of fairly high resistance. A 6V relay taking 50mA will run for weeks on a single unit. The rectifier can be a 1N4001 or virtually any small diode, and the capacitor can be $100\mu F$ or so, 10V or 12V rating, or what chances to be to hand.

For illumination, a handlamp or lantern battery, with its usual voltage bulb (generally 3.5V or 6V) will do well. The items are assembled in a suitable case, with flexible cord and plug, so that it can be left plugged into a convenient outlet. Fit a 2A fuse in the mains plug. If a double-insulated transformer and insulated box are used, a 2-core cable can be employed here. But for a metal box or ordinary (not double-insulated) transformer, use a 3-core cable, so that the box, transformer core, and one secondary lead can be earthed by the yellow-green conductor.

Bell Substitute for Deaf

Deaf persons living alone may use some form of visual indicator light. If this is connected instead of a bell, it will only flash briefly unless the caller holds the push; a similar limitation applies when the light is employed as well as a bell, as a confirmation to the hard-of-hearing. To avoid the light being over-looked, a latch-on circuit can be used for it, as in Figure 13.

Switch A is the usual bell push, and B is normally left closed. When the push is operated, current flows through the relay coil, and the relay contacts close. These contacts now complete the coil circuit, so the relay remains closed, and the lamp in parallel with the relay coil stays illuminated.

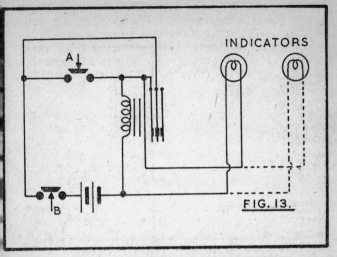

FIG. 13.

The elderly often occupy favourite positions, so that the bulb can be situated where it is likely to be seen almost at once. If necessary, two or more lamps may be used in parallel. Some such circuits switch on the house lighting, with the aid of a mains circuit relay.

Switch B should be placed with the relay and lamp, or in some convenient position so that it can be pressed, to release the relay circuit, when answering the door. The whole may be operated from a 6V battery, for safety and to avoid any need to touch mains wiring.

UJT Delay

Figure 14 uses a capacitor and unijunction transistor to control the relay. This type of transistor has two bases, B1 and B2, and an emitter. In this circuit, current from B2 operates the relay when the voltage across C1 has risen to the point where the UJT is turned on.

With a 2k relay, 12V supply, and $3500\mu F$ at C1 position, the longest interval with VR1 fully in circuit is approximately 3 minutes. Minimum delay is a few seconds. The longest delay possible depends largely on leakage in C1, as when R1/VR1

29

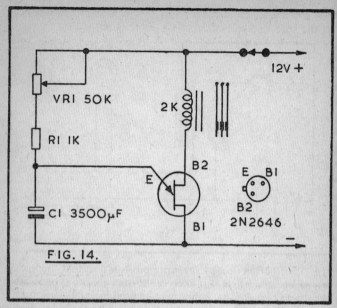

FIG. 14.

total a very high resistance, C1 may never gain enough potential. This is also determined by the UJT emitter current.

The relay may switch an item either on or off after the chosen interval, according to the contacts used.

Direct Relay Light Control

Where relatively low sensitivity is sufficient, a light dependent resistor will provide direct control of a high resistance relay. The LDR is placed in series with the coil winding, as in Figure 15.

Resistance of the LDR falls as illumination increases, and with the ORP12 or similar type, operation of a 2,000 ohm relay should be expected with lighting such as a 40W lamp at 1 foot. Adjustment over the required illumination levels can be obtained by changing the supply voltage, or using a potentiometer to do this. A relay of lower resistance is possible, but a check should be made that the maximum dissipation of the LDR (typically 200mW) is not then exceeded.

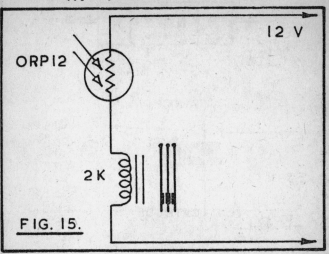

ORP12

12 V

2 K

FIG. 15.

SCRs

Silicon Controlled Rectifiers

The thyristor or silicon controlled rectifier is a device which can be employed in many circuits as it allows a small current or pulse to switch on a much larger current. The essential features of a typical SCR are shown in Figure 16.

The SCR can be regarded as a PNPN structure, as at A. Here, the central region may be regarded as a rectifier N-P, which has further junctions P and N formed each side. When any of the junctions have bias applied in the forward direction, they conduct readily; but if reverse bias is applied, only a small current flows, due to the movement of the minority carriers. This effect is like that obtained with a PN junction rectifier.

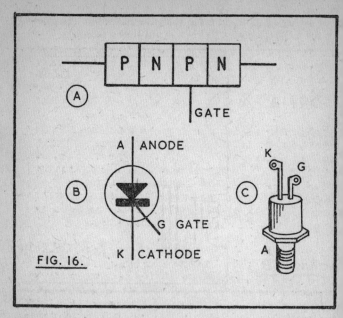

FIG. 16.

If the voltage applied across the device increases, the leakage current increases also, and a point is reached where breakdown occurs. In this state, the SCR is analogous to a saturated transistor and PN junction with forward bias and so the device conducts readily, and can pass a high current.

This breakdown and avalanche effect can be caused by raising the voltage across the SCR to a sufficiently high level. The condition remains until current through the SCR has been reduced to some particular low level, referred to as the holding current.

The same effect can be initiated by supplying current at the gate indicated. This allows a high increase in the forward current and the SCR moves into the "on" state described earlier.

There are thus two methods of changing the SCR from its "off" or non-conducting state to the "on" state. The voltage applied can be raised sufficiently, or an initiating current can be supplied to the gate. The latter generally has the more useful circuit application, as a small gate current can control the flow of a very much larger current through the device. This larger current will continue, even in the absence of gate current, until the current through the SCR falls below the holding level mentioned. The device then returns to its "off" condition.

It will be seen that the SCR operates in a similar manner to a relay, but with important distinctions. Unless arranged to latch on, the relay opens when the coil current is removed, whereas the SCR continues to conduct. There is also no isolation of circuits, as found between coil and contacts of a relay. For this reason, and because more than one circuit may eventually need to be under control, the SCR may on some occasions provide the means of switching a relay.

Figure 16 also shows the usual symbol, and a typical SCR. The smaller type of SCR will have wire lead-outs, but the larger types have a stud as in Figure 16 or some other means of conducting away heat. A small SCR may be suitable for perhaps only 0.5A at 50V, or 1A with a heat sink clip, whereas the larger SCRs can deal with high voltages and currents of many amperes. When a circuit is constructed, there is generally no reason at all why an SCR of higher current and voltage rating than that indicated should not be used. This can allow items to hand to be utilised, or merely give a large safety factor in terms of current and voltage.

SCR Test

It is extremely useful to be able to check the working of a silicon controlled rectifier, as this may easily save troublesome investigation of a circuit which fails to operate. It will also help a proper understanding of the way in which many circuits operate. Newly purchased SCRs, used within their ratings, should of course present no trouble. But if a surplus or scrap box SCR is to be used, a quick test to show that it is working may be well worth while.

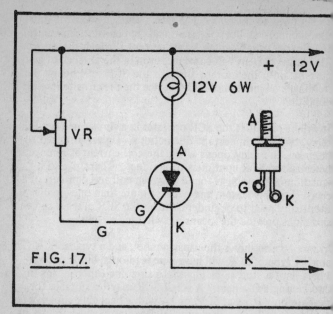

FIG. 17.

Figure 17 shows a 3 ampere 50 volt SCR, and a test circuit.
It is not even necessary that a variable resistor or potentiometer be used, as a fixed resistor can be situated here. Nor
is it necessary that the lamp, or supply voltage, be as shown.
These are merely convenient for the test.

Points G and K are merely temporary connections, so that
these circuits can be interrupted. Assume initially that a fixed
resistor of a few hundred ohms is substituted for VR. When K
is closed, the lamp does not light. When G is also closed, the
lamp lights at about full brilliance. The lamp remains lit in
this way even when G is opened again. But if K is opened
momentarily, the lamp does not light when K is closed again,
but does so when G is closed. This constitutes the "on" and
"off" operation of the SCR.

If VR is connected as shown, and is of quite high value (say
50k) a meter may be placed at G, to show the gate current.
With K closed, slowly reduce the value of VR. A small gate
current will flow, and will rise as the value of VR is reduced.
At some level of gate current the SCR will abruptly commence

34

to conduct, and the bulb will light. With a typical 3A 50V SCR, this was found to happen at approximately 0.5mA gate current. So in this circuit 0.5mA at the gate initiates the 500mA anode-cathode current.

A further test can be made by supplying the circuit from an adjustable voltage source, to find the level at which the SCR is returned to its "off" state. Close K, and temporarily close G, afterwards opening G. Now reduce the supply to some low voltage, such as 2V. Restore to 12V, and note that the bulb still lights. Reduce the potential to, say, 1V, and check as before. At some stage a point will be found where if the supply voltage is reduced below a certain level, the SCR no longer conducts when the full voltage is restored, as it has passed into the "off" condition. In the circuit shown, this was found at about 0.5V.

In some circuits regular restoring of the "off" condition is obtained by this means. As example, in circuits run from AC, where the SCR supply sweeps from zero up to a peak value, then down again to zero, conduction being triggered by a gate pulse, and ceasing when the holding current has fallen below the threshold.

SCR Types

SCRs are available for a whole range of operating voltages and currents. It is only practicable to mention a small number in detail, but this will prove to be a useful guide to the operating conditions for similar types. SCRs of larger rating than required for a circuit can generally be used with success — the main disadvantage of using an unnecessarily large SCR (apart from its slightly greater cost) is that it may require a heavier gate current.

The TO5 type (Fig. 18) is available with 1A rating, for 50V to 400V. Popular ratings are 50V 1A, 100V 1A, 200V 1A, 300V 1A and 400V 1A. If the maximum working voltage rating is exceeded, the device would be expected to break down. The current rating is RMS. Gate potential and current would lie around 3V and 10mA. Maximum sensitivity varies, and is usually important only when a small gate current will

35

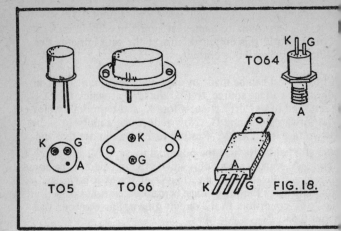

FIG. 18.

be available. The case is common to the anode, and this must not be overlooked if a heat sink or clip is used. This clip is recommended when working near maximum rating, or when the SCR is found to become hot in use.

The TO64 type is available with the same voltages as already quoted, and 3A rating. The threaded stud is common to the anode and allows heat sinking when necessary. Larger types, of similar shape, are available for 4A, 5A, 7A, 10A, 25A and other currents, and up to 400V.

The TO66 type is typically for 5A 400V, while the flat type is available with 400V 4A and other ratings, with heat sink fastening common to the anode, or in some types isolated.

TO5 SCRs will be used in many circuits given here, though the larger SCRs are necessary for circuits where currents are heavier.

Characteristics

By noting the maximum current and other ratings of a typical SCR device, it will be seen how circuits can be arranged for satisfactory operation, yet without any rating being exceeded.

PFV. This is the highest forward voltage which should be present across the SCR with the gate open. With AC derived supplies it is necessary to remember that the peak voltage is approximately 1.414 times the RMS value, and that it is the latter which is shown by an AC meter. So a 400V SCR is usual for 200/250V AC circuits.

I/GT or gate trigger current is the minimum DC value which will switch the device from the off to on condition (typically a few milliamperes).

P/GM or peak gate power dissipation is that between gate and cathode, and is typically a few watts. A gate series resistor will limit this. Average gate power dissipation is similar but found by averaging conditions for one cycle.

I/HO or holding current is the minimum necessary to hold the SCR in the conducting condition, and may be some milliamperes. If the circuit does not provide sufficient holding current, the SCR will revert to the off condition.

P/RV is the peak reverse voltage which can be safely applied with the gate open.

F/V is the forward on voltage, with the device conducting, and is typically around 1V.

V/GT is the gate trigger voltage, or potential necessary to cause avalanche, and often round 0.5 to 1.5V.

Operating conditions are related so that changes to one set of ratings can be expected to modify others, in addition to differences between devices of the same general specification.

Buzzer Substitute

Many circuits incorporate some warning device, such as a lamp, buzzer or bell. These are generally suitable, but there are occasions when an alternative type of warning may be preferred. In these circumstances an audio oscillator is often convenient.

The multivibrator shown at A in Figure 19 can then generally be used. This circuit will operate with a wide range of transistors, supply voltages, and component values. Each transistor

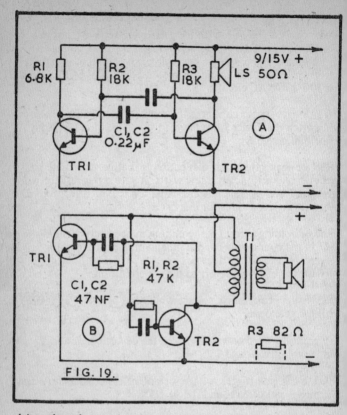

FIG. 19.

drives the other, and audio output is from a small 50 ohm or similar speaker unit. The components, including speaker, are readily assembled in a small box, or the oscillator can be wired on a board or tag-strip which can be included in the case containing the device with which it is used.

The frequency obtained is not very important, provided it is not too low or too high in pitch. If necessary, pitch can be raised by reducing the values of C1, C2, R2 or R3. Pitch is lowered by increasing the values of these components. It is not necessary that C1 and C2 be of the same value; or that R2 and R3 be identical. The transistors may also be dissimilar. It is also in order to use two PNP transistors, instead of the NPN transistors shown, but the supply polarity must then be reversed. Full details of such circuits appear in "Two Transistor Electronic Projects", No. 30 Babani Press.

Figure 19B is another oscillator circuit, which is convenient if a low-impedance speaker and centre-tapped transformer chance to be to hand. A transformer as used for a push-pull output stage, in receivers and small amplifiers, is satisfactory. By using output type transistors and suitable values, considerable volume can be obtained from this circuit. Results are considerably influenced by the characteristics of the transformer T1. Larger values for C1 and C2, or a capacitor across T1 primary, will lower the pitch. R1 and R2 can be adjusted in a similar way to that already described. R3 is to limit current if required and also changes pitch. Transistors as largely used in 500mW and similar output stages are ideal. They can be PNP types if polarity is reversed.

It may well be convenient to assemble either of these circuits with such components as are available, and of approximately similar value to those shown. If a test shows that the sound produced is not satisfactory, some values can then be modified in the way described. The test should be made in conjunction with the control circuit, so that the voltage will be that which is available for the oscillator in the finished equipment.

Mains Supply

Games and other devices which have only occasional and intermittent use can be run from dry batteries. These will have quite a long life, give complete portability, and avoid the use of any mains supplies.

With other devices, which may be left permanently in use, it may be preferred to obtain current from the house mains. There is then no need to check and replace batteries, and over a period the running cost would be expected to be reduced.

The simple mains supply shown in Figure 20 is normally easily adequate for any of the small devices described, and controlled by a relay, thyristor or SCR. Transformer T1 reduces the mains supply to a suitable low voltage, and also isolates the low

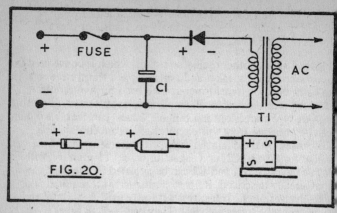

FIG. 20.

voltage circuit from the mains. The rectifier conducts one way only, so that pulsating direct current is obtained, and this is smoothed by capacitor C1 which acts as a reservoir. The output is not pure DC, but is suitable for circuits such as those shown.

It is best to consider the components of the supply individually so that no difficulty will arise in choosing them.

Transformer Bell transformers are ideal for many such circuits and generally have tappings so that 3V, 5V or 8V may be taken. The very small type of transformer is only suitable for a light load, but larger transformers are able to supply several amperes if necessary. Such transformers are sometimes marked with a VA rating. This is the product of Volts and Amperes. As example, an 8 volt 8VA transformer could supply 1 ampere, while an 8 volt 12VA component could supply 1.5 ampere. Where a transformer is of approved double insulated type, no earthing is required. With other transformers, the core and one secondary terminal should be earthed.

Transformers of better type have fuses incorporated, and current can be drawn either from a plug inserted in a convenient outlet, or by permanent wiring. The latter must be arranged as for a bell transformer used with a house chime or bell, so that no shock hazards arise.

With many circuits the exact working voltage is not very critical. Secondary voltages are normally RMS values, and the

40

peak rectified voltage obtainable is up to about 1.414 times this. So about 4.2V would be expected from a 3V winding, with 7V DC from a 5V winding, and 11.2V DC from an 8V winding. Similarly, a 12V transformer would provide approximately 17V DC.

Rectifier A 1A 50PIV silicon diode will be suitable for up to 1 ampere, with a transformer of up to 15V RMS. For larger supplies, use a 2 ampere 100 volt diode, or as required. Such rectifiers are inexpensive so can easily be of adequate rating. A full-wave bridge rectifier may be used instead, if wished. Its AC tags or leads go to T1 secondary, and its positive and negative connections to positive and negative of C1.

Capacitor This is generally about 470µF to 5000µF, and about 1000µF or 2000µF is normally satisfactory. Rather small values do not provide so smooth an output. The capacitor voltage rating should be at least 1.5 times the secondary RMS voltage — a 12V or 15V capacitor would do well for 8V, or a 20V or 25V capacitor for a circuit with a 12V secondary.

A 1A, 2A or other appropriate fuse may be included as shown, to protect the rectifier and transformer if a short circuit arises.

Burglar Alarm

Pressure mats can be purchased which make contact to close a circuit when stepped upon, and with the addition of a bell and SCR can form an effective burglar or intruder alarm. A single pressure mat can be placed under a carpet or rug at a doorway, or in a passage or corridor, or at the foot of the stairs. Even momentary weight on it will then set the bell ringing until switched off by hand.

With the circuit in Figure 21 the alarm circuit is connected to SCR gate, and positive. Pressure on the mat closes this circuit, thus causing the SCR to conduct so that the bell rings. When the gate current ceases the bell continues to ring, as explained earlier.

D1 is to protect the SCR from back emf from the bell windings. As the vibrating contacts of the bell open, thus breaking

41

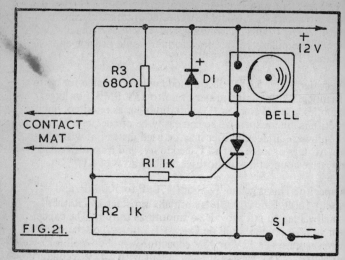

FIG.21.

the circuit, R3 maintains a current through the SCR, so that it does not resume the off condition.

R2 is not necessary when there is negligible leakage in the alarm circuit. Leakage here could provide enough current for the gate to trigger the SCR, but with R2 present leakage would have to be severe before this happens. When the alarm circuit is actually completed, R2 is simply across the supply and has no effect on working.

Current drawn by the circuit, when the bell is not ringing, is negligible. S1 is necessary, to switch off once the circuit has been actuated, and during the day. Supplies of other than 12V may be used.

Two or more pressure mats can be connected in parallel. Other contact devices, such as those which complete a circuit when a door is opened, may be used as well.

Construction

More detailed constructional information of the alarm will be of aid to those who have not built many items of this kind, and will also indicate how later circuits can be assembled.

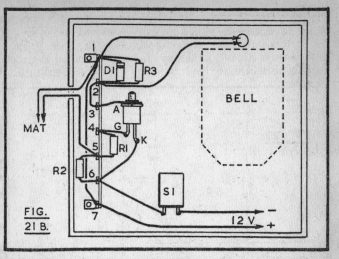

FIG. 21 B.

It is convenient to assemble the components on a tag strip, as in Figure 21B. This can then be fitted in a wooden, plastic or metal box, with the bell mounted on the front. (With a metal box, note that tags 1 and 7 are connected by the mounting.)

A twin insulated lead of any length runs from tags 1 and 5, to the pressure mat. The case can be large enough to house a battery, if mains running is not wanted. If a box is made, 6mm or similar plywood will be satisfactory, and the pieces can be fixed together with woodworking adhesive and a few small panel pins. The back can be attached with screws, so that it can be removed.

The voltage may depend on the bell, and in most instances a 6V supply will be satisfactory. The SCR is mounted by the leads, and a stout wire or tag at the stud (anode) end.

There would be no need to follow the exact layout shown, as numerous other forms of construction would be equally suitable.

Broken Circuit Alarm

Many burglar alarm circuits are so arranged, that a bell is rung when a circuit is broken or interrupted. Doors and windows are fitted with switches which break circuit, when a door or

43

window is opened. With this method, a conductor runs to each switch or circuit breaker in turn, then passes back to the control device. Cutting the conductor will also activate the alarm, so with shops it may continue as a foil strip cemented to glass doors or elsewhere, so that it is broken if the glass is smashed.

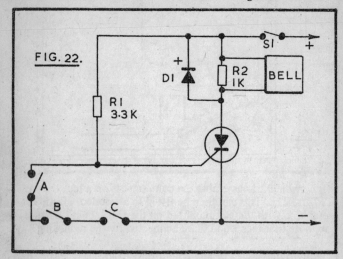

FIG. 22.

In Figure 22 switches A, B and C are shown in series in this way. Any number of switches, contact breakers and similar devices can be used, and all are wired in series. Small push switches which may be set in a wooden door or window frame are available, and these are held in the on position when the door or window is closed. It is not difficult to make various contact devices which are normally closed, but which will break circuit when disturbed.

A small current is available through R1, but is not available for the SCR gate so long as all the devices A, B and C are closed and this circuit is intact. Opening any of these switches or interrupting the circuit triggers the SCR.

For the home, a doorbell of quite loud type, as generally used with an 8V or similar transformer, can be fitted. Resistor R2 passes a continuous current to hold the SCR on, so that the bell remains ringing with only a momentary interruption of the circuit A, B or C. Without R2, the bell will stop should A, B or C be closed, or the circuit be restored. D1 is to suppress back emf generated by the bell mechanism.

S1 is necessary to turn the SCR off. The whole device can be constructed in a box on which the bell is mounted. It may run from its own battery, or preferably from the mains, as described elsewhere. The warning circuit may take in garage doors, workshop, or whatever is required.

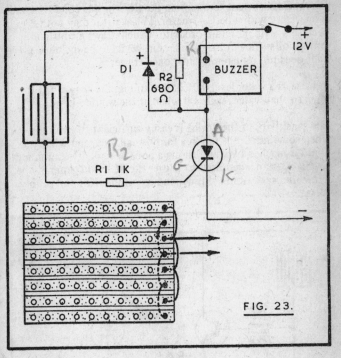

FIG. 23.

Rain Alarm

The device shown in Figure 23 operates in a similar way to the burglar alarm, except that a rain sensor pad is used. It can also be employed to indicate when the level of water in a pool or elsewhere has risen to the wanted height.

The sensor pad is made from 0.1in or 0.15in pitch Veroboard, with alternate conductive strips joined, as shown. A board about 3 x 2 in (75 x 50mm) is convenient, and a twin flexible lead is soldered to one end of the sensor, to run to the alarm. The board is placed with conductive strips uppermost. Rain falling on the board reduces the circuit resistance until the gate current triggers the SCR. This sounds the buzzer, which remains on until the switch is opened.

R2 provides current to maintain the SCR in this condition and is necessary with a bell or buzzer. This resistor may not be necessary with an audio oscillator which draws a continuous current of sufficient magnitude, but needs to be included if the SCR does not remain on when once triggered.

For use as a water level indicator warning, the sensor pad is hung so that water reaches it when at the wanted level.

The sensitivity of the device is easily sufficient for warning when some raindrops fall in a fairly small area, and when the board is reached by water filling a pool or tank. The minimum circuit resistance required to trigger the SCR will generally be a few thousand ohms, this depending on the SCR and supply voltage.

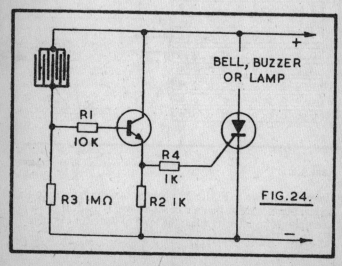

FIG.24.

If it is wished to boost sensitivity, this can be done by adding the transistor amplifier shown, Figure 24. Operation can then be obtained with a sensor resistance as high as 1 megohm or more.

TR1 is a general purpose audio or similar transistor, with hfe (current amplification factor) of 100 to 500 or so. In the absence of base current the transistor does not conduct, and there is no voltage drop across R2. When current is able to flow through the sensor pad to base, TR1 conducts and a voltage drop arises across R2, moving the SCR gate positive, to trigger it.

With this circuit, insulation at the pad and circuit to it must be good, because sensitivity is so high. Sensitivity can be reduced by fitting R3, which may be 1 megohm or lower in value; or by reducing the value of R2; or by using a transistor with a lower hfe.

All the components, including buzzer and battery, but not the sensor pad, can be assembled in a small case. For use as a rain alarm, the pad is out-of-doors. The device itself should be placed where it will immediately be heard, if drying washing is to be brought in should rain commence.

Audio Oscillator

A silicon controlled rectifier can be used as an audio oscillator by employing the circuit in Figure 25. C1 charges through R1, and when the gate level, derived through VR1, is sufficiently high, the SCR is triggered. Current flows through the SCR and speaker, and so discharges C1 and the SCR anode voltage and current fall to a low level, so that the SCR ceases to conduct until the cycle is repeated.

VR1 allows the gate potential obtained from the voltage across C1 to be adjusted, and this changes the frequency. The values fitted for R1 and C1 also influence the frequency, as does the SCR.

This circuit is suitable for a Morse oscillator, with a pair of 8 ohm or similar headphones. The key is placed in one connection to the battery, which can be 9V. Current drain is small.

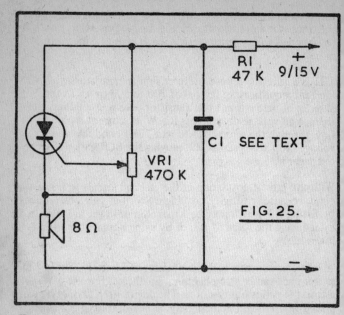

R1
47 K   9/15 V

C1   SEE TEXT

VR1
470 K

8 Ω

FIG. 25.

To secure a suitable pitch, C1 can be 0.22μF. (Any value around this is satisfactory, as VR1 allows considerable adjustment in pitch.)

The oscillator can be used as a low level loudspeaker warning device instead of a bell or buzzer, or in conjunction with a lamp. The sound output level is rather small with a speaker, but is enough for some purposes. C1 may be increased to about 1μF to 4μF, the larger values resulting in a much lower frequency. The supply voltage can also be considerably greater than when using the circuit for a headphone oscillator. Audio output could be increased by adding a transistor amplifier.

Zener Triggered Oscillator

A further audio oscillator giving reasonably loud speaker volume is shown in Figure 26. When the circuit is switched on, C1 charges through VR1 and R3, so that the potential across D1 rises. When D1 conducts, gate current is supplied to the

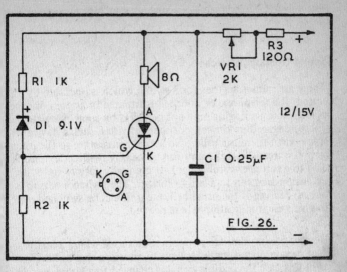

FIG. 26.

SCR, triggering it. C1 then discharges through the SCR and
speaker, and the voltage across C1 falls to zero. At the same
time, the SCR ceases to conduct. The cycle is then repeated
C1 repeatedly charging until the SCR is triggered. R3 limits
the maximum current possible through the speaker and SCR,
with VR1 at minimum resistance.

The supply voltage must be somewhat higher than the zener
diode voltage, and the latter need not be 9.1V. The frequency
of operation increases as the value of VR1 is reduced. However, working conditions must not be such that the SCR does
not turn off, which will happen if the total resistance VR1
and R3 is very low.

Increasing the capacitance of C1 lowers the working frequency.
Smaller values here increase the frequency, but low values tend
to reduce the volume obtained.

This circuit can be made to operate with a wide range of component values, and at repetition rates of from several thousand
hertz to one per second or slower, C1 being increased to 47μF
to 470μF for the very slow speeds. If the circuit fails to
operate with other values, C1 should be checked for leakage,
and a meter in series with the speaker will show if current

through VR1/R3 remains at a steady value high enough to hold the SCR on.

Sound Operated Switch

There are numerous uses for a switch which is operated by sound. If a telephone or doorbell is situated in a room or other place where its ringing may not be heard by someone watching TV, or engaged in kitchen or other activities, such a device will show when there is a caller. No actual connection to the phone or bell is needed, as the unit can be nearby, with an extension lead to a suitable warning light. It is equally easy to have the extension lead run to a bell or buzzer. Then when a person is out of hearing of the usual bell, the unit can be switched on, to give a clear indication where needed.

Devices of this kind are also sometimes used where a badly deaf person may sometimes have to answer a ring or knock, as in this case the audible signal is changed to a visual one. In fact, two or more indicator lamps can be used in different locations, if necessary.

The circuit in Figure 27 is a simple one, but sufficiently sensitive for these purposes. Sounds are picked up by a small loudspeaker — a 2½ or 3½ in (65 or 90mm) unit is convenient here, and the speaker should be of quite high impedance. Low impedance units will give a smaller signal voltage, so will reduce sensitivity. C1 is necessary so as not to upset base bias for TR1, obtained through R1.

The amplified signal available across R2 is taken to D1 by C2. Audio signals at D1 are rectified, to provide negative bias for the PNP transistor TR2. This bias causes TR2 to conduct, so that current to trigger the SCR is provided for the gate. VR1 is used to adjust operating conditions, and also sensitivity.

R3 and C3 provide a small delay in operating voltage for TR1 and TR2. Without this, the circuit may be triggered by the sound of switching on, or by the current surge.

To set up the circuit, have VR1 at quite low resistance. After switching on, carefully rotate VR1 to increase the resistance

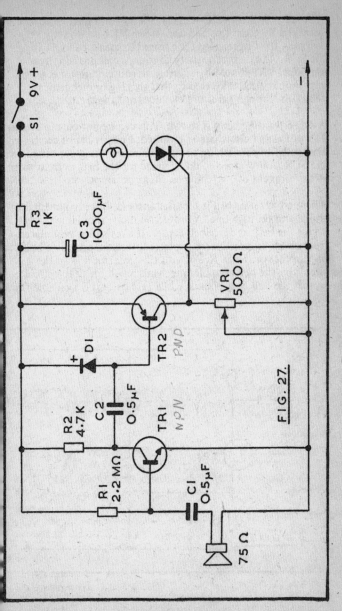

FIG. 27.

in circuit, until the SCR triggers. VR1 should then be turned back slightly from this position. When VR1 is correctly set, snapping the fingers about 2ft from the speaker should trigger the SCR. As excess sensitivity to sounds can prove to be a nuisance, VR1 should be adjusted to suit circumstances. The unit should also be located so that shaking or mechanical vibration through furniture etc. does not trigger it.

A single warning lamp is shown. This can be put on top of the TV, or located elsewhere as required. Further lamps can be connected in parallel, up to the maximum rating permitted by the SCR. Allowance should be made for the high current surge, at the moment of switching on filament lamps.

Where a buzzer or bell is required instead, this is connected to anode and positive line. A protective diode should be used across the bell, as described earlier. If a resistor is also placed from anode to positive, as explained, this can provide a holding on current for the SCR. Without this, interruption of the circuit by the bell trembler mechanism will break the circuit, so that the bell only sounds while gate current is available from TR2.

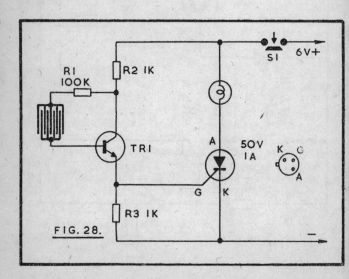

FIG. 28.

6V Touchswitch

The circuit in Figure 28 is operated by touch, and has various applications. With a 6V battery supply and 6V 3W or similar lamp, as shown, it can be used as a child's bedside light.

The touchpad normally provides no base current for TR1, as it is a complete insulator. When the pad is touched, leakage across it supplies base current through R1 and R2, so that TR1 conducts. Emitter current triggers the SCR, so that the lamp is lit. The circuit remains in this condition until the push switch S1 is pressed. With values as indicated, the circuit will operate with a resistance of some megohms across the pad, which is so made that it can be touched anywhere over its area. Higher sensitivity would be easily arranged, but a point is reached where extremely slight leakage through the pad for any reason will actuate the SCR.

The pad is easily made from perforated board having strip conductors, as it is only necessary to use foils 1, 3, 5...etc. for one side of the circuit, and foils 2, 4, 6...etc. for the other side. (See Fig. 23) This is done by soldering on bridging connections passing through the holes to the insulated side of the board, at the same time running leads from foils 1 and 2. Board with 0.1 in matrix is most suitable, using a pad about 2 x 1 in (50 x 25mm) fitted to the top of the case which contains the battery and other items.

Adjustable Grip Tester

This novelty shows the strength of a person's grip in terms of lowered electrical resistance, Figure 29. As such, it is not a true indicator of strength, but can nevertheless be used for amusing tests of this kind. It has an adjustable "strength" control, which can be set to higher and higher levels, until all but one person has been eliminated. Success, at each test level, is shown by an indicator lamp.

The grip device is made as described later, and is connected between positive and R1. R1 limits base current, should VR1 be at maximum sensitivity and the tester be shorted deliberately with a metal object. The resistance provided across the gripping device falls as the grip is increased, and can be 200k or less with a strong grip. VR1 provides adjustment of sensit-

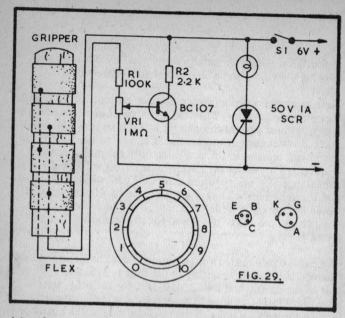

FIG. 29.

ivity, from the point where lightly holding the gripper activates the circuit, to a level where operation is virtually impossible. Sensitivity is minimum with VR1 wiper at negative. Rotation of the potentiometer allows the combined resistance from transistor base to positive line to become more and more effective. When base current via the gripper and R1 is sufficient, TR1 conducts to trigger the SCR. This lights the bulb, to indicate success at this level, until S1 is opened.

VR1 should be a linear potentiometer, with a large knob and scale. This scale is calibrated in empirical units of "strength" from 1 to 25, the latter being with VR1 slider at negative. A case with a sloping front, having this dial on the panel, is suggested.

The gripper needs to be strongly made, and it is attached to a metre or so of twin flex. It is made from broomhandle or dowel about ¾ in to 1 in (20 x 25mm) in diameter, and 5 in or 125mm long. Cut four strips of clean tinplate ½ in (13mm) wide and long enough to go round the dowel. They must be free of sharp edges and can be rubbed with emery paper to achieve this (avoid cutting the fingers). Saw channels to take the leads shown, and drill a hole so that the flex can emerge at one end of the handle. Draw the strips as tightly as possible round the wood, and solder the overlap and connections. A space of about $^3/_{16}$th inch (5mm) is left between the rings. Lateral movement can be avoided by tapping in a few small panel pins or sprigs. As the grip is tightened, a greater area of the hand comes into contact with the strips, and the resistance between hand and strips falls.

Tests can begin with VR1 at 1, so that the way in which the device operates is demonstrated. Each time VR1 is advanced, all competitors try their "strength" and in due course some will be unable to succeed.

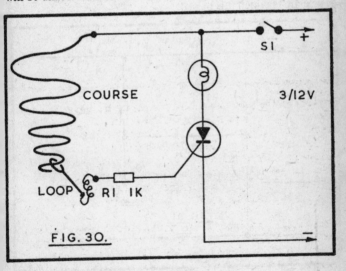

FIG. 30.

Silent "Steady Hand"

The "steady hand" game is described in the section on relays (Fig. 10) and can be a trial of eye and nerve of almost any chosen difficulty. The modification shown in Figure 30 uses a red lamp as an indication of failure instead of the bell or buzzer, with a silicon controlled rectifier as the triggered device.

As will be seen from the circuit, gate current is only available via R1 when the ring is in contact with the shaped conductor which forms the hazard along which the ring is moved. The degree of difficulty rests on the convolutions and length of the conductor, and the clearance provided by the ring.

A 50V 1A SCR is employed, and the operating voltage can be anything from 3V to 12V or so. The lamp is chosen to suit. For a small 3V or 4.5V dry battery, a 3.5V torch bulb is suitable, and a 6V, 6.3V, 12V or other lamp can be fitted for higher voltage supplies.

This form of indicator will be preferred for children's games, where a buzzer or bell may be unwanted. Switch S1 is necessary so that the SCR can be turned off, once it has been triggered by failure to keep the ring out of contact with the course along which it is passed.

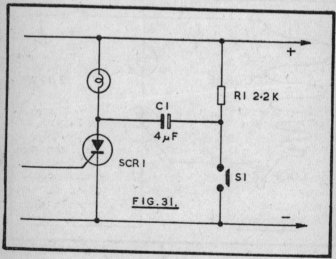

FIG. 31.

OFF Switching SCRs

When a silicon controlled rectifier has been triggered into the on condition, this continues until anode current has been interrupted or reduced to a low level. With unsmoothed supplies derived by rectification of AC, interruption arises each cycle or half-cycle, depending on the type of rectification. In other circuits, where continuous DC is present, a switch may be used to interrupt current.

Another method, which does not involve breaking the circuit, is to employ a capacitor as in Figure 31. It is assumed that SCR1 is conducting, so C1 is charged to approximately the supply voltage and has the polarity shown. When S1 is closed, the positive side of C1 is common to the cathode, so the capacitor charge momentarily moves the SCR anode to zero or negative, thus switching it off.

S1 may be a push-switch, relay, or another SCR as in the next circuit. In Figure 31 C1 is an electrolytic capacitor, but in some circuits a reversible component is necessary here.

SCR Flasher

Figure 32 is a circuit which flashes a 12V 2.2W lamp at approximately one second intervals. The periodicity of operation can be modified by changing the value of R1, or C1. Pulses are available from B1, and are taken to the SCR gates by C2 and C3.

When SCR2 is conducting and the lamp is lit, the polarity across C4 allows triggering of SCR1 to turn SCR2 off, in the way described earlier. Both SCRs do not turn on simultaneously, due to the different anode loads, and R4 can be large enough to prevent SCR1 remaining in the on condition. SCR2 thus has alternate on and off periods. With the values shown, the commutating capacitor C4 cannot be under $1\mu F$ or SCR2 may remain permanently on. The capacitor must be reversible, and $2\mu F$ or larger may be fitted.

The circuit will operate with quite a range of supply voltages, but commutation ceases if the potential is reduced to about 6V. Flashing is at half the UJT frequency.

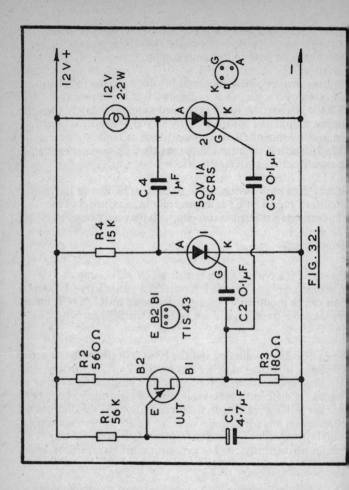

FIG. 32.

Train and Model Control

By incorporating a silicon controlled rectifier in the power supply for a model train full adjustment of speed may be provided. Better slow speed starting and running at low speed is obtained than with a resistance controller. There are several reasons for this improvement. With a series resistance controller the voltage dropped depends on the current flowing, which is unusually high when the train is about to start, or when friction rises. Thus the voltage applied to the motor is lower just at those times when power ought to be maintained. One result is that the train usually starts with a rush; another, that it stalls with a slight extra load, when running very slowly.

With SCR control adjusted for slow running, power reaches the motor only during a part of each cycle. This gives greater torque at low speed so that the engine can be crept forwards. The circuit here (Figure 33) also provides an increase in motor power when the load on the motor rises, because current rises when the load resistance falls, which is exactly the opposite effect to that of the series resistance type of controller.

T1 is the mains transformer, which will generally be about 15V 1A unless the layout is comprehensive and has several trains likely to operate from the same supply. For the usual model engine, a transformer delivering about 14V to 18V is suitable.

Full wave rectification is provided, either by a bridge rectifier rated at 50V 1A minimum, or by means of four 1N4001 or similar individual rectifiers. It is of course perfectly in order for the transformer or rectifiers to be of 2A or other rating higher than 1A. This would not mean that a higher current must be drawn, but merely that it would be available, if wanted.

Current reaches the model through the SCR. The rectifier output is pulsating DC at 100 Hertz, and the SCR is triggered into conduction for a part of each cycle. With VR1 wiper towards the end marked R2 a triggering current is obtained early in each cycle, but as the wiper is moved towards negative, triggering is delayed. So VR1 controls the length of pulses obtained, and hence the total power.

C1 provides some smoothing of the output. The bulb is simply for short circuit protection. If a 12V 12W lamp is fitted, current cannot exceed 1A. With permanently connected models (e.g. not trains) short circuit protection is not necessary.

Whether or not a resistor is required at R2 depends on the output voltage of the transformer and rectifier. If it is found that the model is running at full speed with the wiper of VR1 still

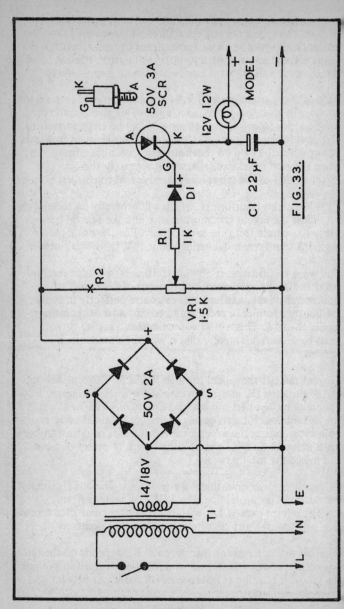

FIG. 33.

60

some distance from this end of the element, then R2 can be added. If R2 is chosen so that full speed is provided with VR1 fully in this direction a smooth, spread-out adjustment of running will be obtained by VR1. R2 will generally be about 200 ohm to 1k.

Actual components are not very critical, nor are the values. The usual 2-pole reversing switch may be fitted in the output circuit. In some cases it may be practical to add the control portion of the unit to an existing transformer/rectifier power supply.

Safety precautions described earlier for mains circuits should be followed, so that no danger of mains shocks can arise.

Control by Light

Various devices which are operated by the intensity of illumination can incorporate a silicon controlled rectifier as the means of switching on or off a lamp or other indicator, or bringing into use alternative illumination.

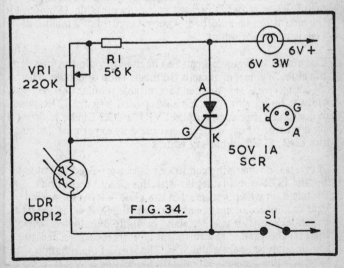

FIG. 34.

A light dependent resistor or LDR may be used as the control device. The ORP12 will be suitable. When not illuminated, this has a resistance of 1 megohm or more. When illuminated, the resistance falls, and can become under a few hundred ohms with fairly strong lighting such as that from a 40W lamp at about 2ft. Other similar LDRs are also suitable, and their working can easily be checked by measuring their resistance with varying degrees of illumination.

Figure 34 shows one method of obtaining control in such a way that when the general level of illumination falls, a bulb is switched on. While light is reaching the LDR, its resistance is low, so that the SCR gate voltage is only very slightly positive, relative to the cathode. The SCR remains off until illumination of the LDR falls, causing its resistance to rise, thus raising the gate voltage. At some point gate current reaches a high enough level for the SCR to conduct, completing the circuit to the bulb.

VR1 allows fine adjustment of sensitivity. The bulb and battery voltage need not be as shown. Such a device forms a type of emergency light, which comes on when other lighting fails or becomes insufficient. It may be used as a child's light, and can be run from a low voltage supply derived from the mains. When battery operated, it is fully portable. If preferred, the circuit can be modified to permit control of a mains voltage lamp, as shown later.

The circuit in Figure 34 can also be used in various games or novelties. Typical of these is the magic lamp or candle, where all components are enclosed in a suitable tubular or other case, and the bulb lights when a hand is passed over the LDR, which is concealed. For such purposes VR1 and R1 can be replaced by a resistor whose value is best found by experiment, to suit the LDR, SCR and battery voltage.

A reversal of operating conditions can be arranged by connecting the LDR as in Figure 35. With this circuit, the bulb is switched on when light reaches the LDR. VR1 is set so that gate current is not sufficient to trigger the SCR when the light dependent resistor is in the dark, or dimly illuminated. When light on the LDR is at a sufficient level its resistance becomes low enough to operate the SCR. The level of illumination at which this happens depends on the setting of VR1.

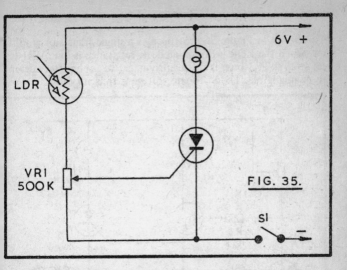

LDR

VRI
500K

6V +

FIG. 35.

SI

The main use for such a circuit would be in toys or games, or to give warning when a light which is normally off is turned on, or for an electronic slave flash for photography. A bell or buzzer may be substituted for the bulb, as described elsewhere. This warning device can be at any distance from the control circuit.

With both circuits, a push switch or switch of ordinary type is required at S1, to interrupt the circuit.

Both these circuits can be set for quite good sensitivity, so that they operate when daylight begins to fail, or when ordinary room lighting is switched on or off. No special precautions, such as shielding the LDR from the lamp in Figure 34 are necessary.

For greater sensitivity, a transistor amplifier can be added. This allows response to smaller changes in illumination.

Sensitive Light Operated Switch

The circuit in Figure 36 incorporates a single transistor amplifier. When the LDR is illuminated, its resistance is low. VR1 is set so that TR1 base is sufficiently negative for emitter current to be negligible. The SCR gate voltage is thus very low.

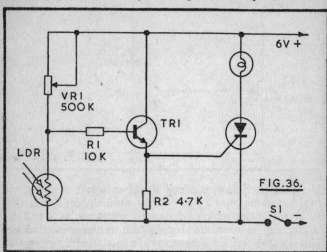

FIG.36.

As illumination falls the LDR resistance rises and the base of TR1 moves positive. Increasing emitter current through R2 shifts the SCR gate in a positive direction, until conduction is initiated.

Many NPN transistors will be suitable here, especially medium and high gain types such as the BC107. Component values are not critical, and other supply voltages are suitable. The adjustment of VR1 is most easily made by slightly shading the LDR with the hand, meanwhile rotating VR1 to secure the necessary working conditions.

Uses for this circuit are similar to those of the earlier circuit where failing light turns the circuit on.

As before, conditions may be changed so that a rise in lighting level switches the circuit on, as in Figure 37. This has a similar transistor amplifier, but emitter current rises when the LDR is

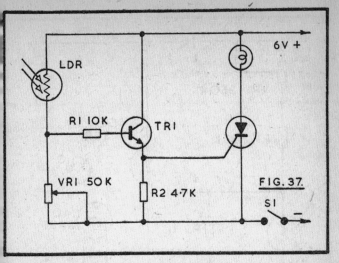

FIG. 37.

lit, thus triggering the SCR. Uses for this circuit are similar to those for Figure 35 but with greater sensitivity.

If a relay coil is substituted for the lamp in these circuits, a further circuit can be completed by contacts which are normally closed. The controlled circuit will thus be opened when the relay is energised. This allows a lamp or other item to be switched off, instead of on, by either a rise or fall in general illumination.

Mains Light Operated Circuit

Figure 38 is a circuit giving direct control of a mains voltage lamp. It will generally be used for a child's room, or to switch on a light automatically when a house is empty, or to illuminate a door, path, etc. when darkness falls.

A 1N4004 400V 1A rectifier is convenient for D1, but any other small rectifier of sufficient voltage rating is suitable here. The SCR is a 400V 1A type.

VR1 and R1 in series form one arm of the potential divider, and the LDR and R2 in parallel the other arm. With failing light, the LDR resistance rises until the gate is triggered. The

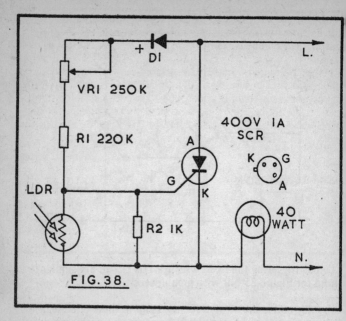

FIG. 38.

values of VR1 and R1 are not too critical, provided the circuit can be adjusted to come on at the wanted point. R1 can be modified, if necessary, to suit the LDR and SCR, or working conditions. If VR1 and R1 are of too low value, the circuit will tend to switch on whatever the level of illumination.

The circuit can be built in a small space, especially if VR1 and R1 are replaced by a fixed resistor. Here, 330k should be suitable, but a test will have to be made to check that the circuit works as required. One method is to adjust VR1 for operation at the light level required, then measure this and R1 with a meter, to find the nearest standard value to fit.

Construction should place the LDR behind or away from the light-bulb. With AC mains, current repeatedly passes through zero, so the SCR is not kept on and the lamp only remains lit when the LDR is in dim light. As a result, the lamp ceases to be lit when the general level of illumination rises again.

With this circuit, the lamp cannot light at full brilliance. But the lighting obtained will generally be adequate for the purposes mentioned.

Reference should be made to earlier notes on the safety of mains operated equipment. All components for this circuit are readily enclosed in an insulated junction box, or other strong case. It should be impossible to touch any components or connections. A skirted lampholder can be fitted to the case for the lamp, and a flexible cord can then run to a mains outlet.

Audio Light Modulator

A light modulator adds interest to a disco, or can be put on for a party or amusement at home. It can be single channel for general audio, 2-channel for treble and bass, or 3-channel for treble, middle and bass frequencies. Illumination can be of any chosen colours, such as blue, green and yellow for bass, middle and treble, or red and green for bass and treble. For a single channel, the light could be any colour, or incorporated in a psychedilic fitting.

Mains voltage lamps of about 40W to 100W will generally be used, though there is no reason why low voltage bulbs should not be employed should this be preferred.

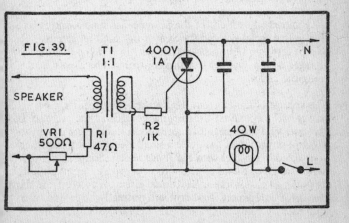

The lamps flash on and off in time with the musical beat, or in accord with the peaks of volume at various frequencies. This is quite effective with even a single coloured lamp, but it is much more entertaining with two or three lamps, and frequency-sensitive control circuits.

Figure 39 shows a single lamp audio light modulator, and this is easily developed for one or two further bulbs. The audio driving power required for a single lamp is not very great, and could if wished be obtained from any tape or record player (or radio) with an output of 1 watt or so. The audio signal is taken from the loudspeaker circuit to the isolating transformer T1. A similar signal thus arises in the secondary of this transformer.

Current for the lamp is obtained through the SCR. When low level audio is present in T1, the SCR is not triggered into conduction. However, a loud beat, or sustained higher volume, drives the gate sufficiently for the SCR to conduct, so the lamp lights to follow the sounds. As the SCR circuit operates from AC, the SCR moves out of the avalanche condition whenever the gate current is low.

If this circuit is scaled down to use 12V or other low voltages, current must be derived from a mains transformer. A direct current supply is not suitable, as the lamp will remain fully lit, once the SCR has been triggered.

VR1 allows adjustment of the power reaching T1, and is set so that with normal volume the SCR is triggered repeatedly, except during quiet passages. The way in which performance changes with adjustment of this control will be clear when using the circuit.

The voltage obtained from the speaker circuit, for a given power, will depend on the impedance. Due to the presence of R1 (and VR1) the circuit is normally suitable for a 2 ohm to 16 ohm output, and has quite a small effect on results, when connected in parallel with the loudspeaker. Some equipment may have an optional 2/8 ohm or other spare output circuit, but such an extension or additional circuit is absent from most transistor equipment. No harm will normally be caused to an amplifier by connecting the audio light modulator, as R1 prevents much overall reduction in impedance. Leads should be clear of any pick-up or input circuits, to avoid instability or feedback (in a similar manner to wiring a loudspeaker). If necessary, R1 can be placed at the loudspeaker end of the circuit, or a similar resistor may be inserted here in both leads. so that actual connections to T1 are less prone to cause feedback.

It is not essential that T1 should have a 1:1 ratio. A suitable transformer here is the loudspeaker coupling type, and if this has two secondaries for 3 ohm or similar speakers, these will provide the 1:1 ratio shown. Where the ratio available is not 1:1, it will generally be necessary to connect it to step-up the primary signal voltage, unless the impedance of the speaker circuit is fairly high. A multirange meter, suitable for audio frequencies and connected to the secondary, should kick up to several volts, with normal volume. If a transformer is to be wound, there is considerable latitude in the number of turns, and about one hundred for primary, and a similar number for the secondary, will be satisfactory. The power handling capacity need not be very great, but wire of about 24swg is convenient.

It is essential that the primary/secondary insulation of the component is adequate to isolate the mains circuit, so small 1:3 and similar transistor coupling transformers are not suitable.

When building a circuit which incorporates audio and mains in this way, safety must be assured as described elsewhere. A breakdown in T1 could place mains voltages on the audio and speaker circuit, but with many amplifiers the primary of T1 cannot be earthed for safety. A valve type transformer will generally have insulation intended for several hundred volts, and the core can also be earthed to the mains earth. A low-rating fuse should be fitted in the L conductor. Maximum safety is obtained when the amplifier is also mains operated, with one side of the speaker circuit earthed, so that the primary of T1 may also be earthed.

The alternative to these precautions, which are essential for safety in the event of component failure, is to use lower wattage lamps and draw current for them from a 24V transformer or similar safe low voltage source. One pole of the lamp supply, or a centre-tap, can then be earthed for protection.

The capacitors are to suppress interference produced by the SCR. Values here are not too critical, but the components should be 600V to 1kV rating.

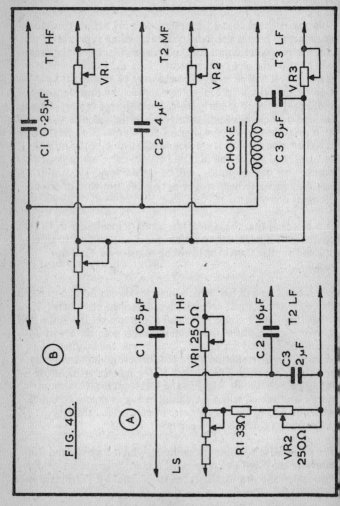

FIG. 40.

Multi-Channel

For high frequency and low frequency channels, the circuit at
A in Figure 40 may be used. C1 is a HF pass capacitor, supplying the transformer T1. Loss of HF through the LF channel
is reduced by R1 and VR2. The LF channel transformer T2 is
driven through the larger capacitor C2 whose reactance is small
at these frequencies, and higher frequencies are reduced by C3.
VR1 and VR2 allow an initial setting up of the relative sensit-
ivities of the treble (HF) and bass (LF) circuits. The two SCR
circuits are as already shown, with lamps of different colour.

At B, frequency discrimination is provided for three channels.
The HF channel is operated through C1 and the middle frequency channel through C2. The LF channel has the parallel
capacitor C3, which suppresses high frequencies in conjunction
with the choke. This item may be about 1mH to 2.5mH.
VR1/2/3 are for individual adjustment of the level at which the
SCRs trigger and may be 250 ohm each.

The performance of these circuits will be influenced by the
transformers. Adequate drive from the speaker circuit is needed
for the two and three channels. If a shift in the general frequency response is wanted, sensitivity of the HF channel to lower
frequencies may be reduced by making C1 of smaller value.
Very small values will reduce sensitivity, but VR1 can compen-
sate for this to some extent. The middle channel will tend to
be wide. Its LF response can be reduced by having a smaller
value at C2, and it may also have a parallel choke similar to that
for the LF channel, at the T2 side of C2. Response to treble of
the LF circuit can be raised by reducing C3, or having a lower
inductance choke.

Complete separation of frequencies is not of course provided
and is not required. But the difference in response of the three
lamps to HF, MF and LF should be quite apparent.

Delayed Circuits

SCR control can be adopted for delayed circuits, which may
turn either on or off after an interval. The delayed "on" type
of switch is the simpler. One use for it is in quiz games — the
switch is operated, and the contestant must answer before the
bulb lights.

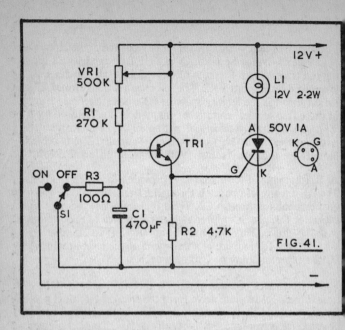

FIG. 41.

Figure 41 is a circuit of this kind. The timing interval begins
when switch S1 is moved to the "on" position. This complete
the battery circuit, and C1 begins to charge through VR1 and
R1. As a result, the base of TR1 moves in a positive direction,
until emitter current begins to flow. When emitter current is
large enough, the voltage drop across R2 is sufficient for the
SCR gate to have reached the level at which the SCR switches
on, so L1 lights.

S1 is a 2-way switch so that C1 is discharged when the device
off, so that the same interval is repeated. With the component
values shown, the interval is adjustable from about 15 to 30
seconds. The exact time depends somewhat on TR1, and other
factors. It can be lengthened by increasing the value of C1, or
increasing the total series resistance VR1/R1. However, if C1
is exceptionally large and has significant leakage, a point will
be reached where the circuit does not come on, though delays
of well over 30 seconds can be provided if wanted. For shorter
intervals, reduce C1 or R1 in value.

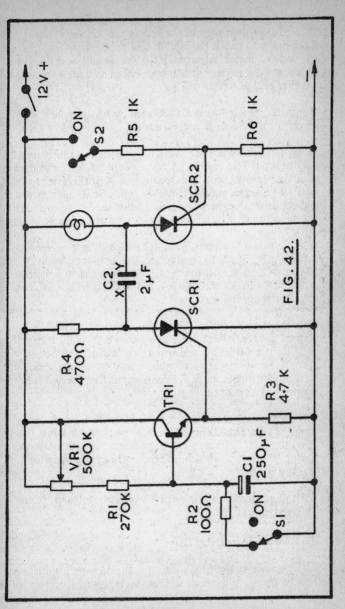

FIG. 42.

73

Any high gain NPN transistor should be suitable here, and it is not necessary that the bulb or supply voltage be as shown. If it is necessary to check the circuit, this can be done by temporarily placing a meter between TR1 collector and positive. If no significant rise in current is found within an interval of switching on, check C1 as mentioned.

If required, the lamp can be replaced by a buzzer, bell, or relay, in the manner described earlier.

To obtain a delay in "off" switching the circuit in Figure 42 may be used. TR1 and SCR1 form a delayed "on" circuit, as with the previous unit. This means that X of C2 is normally at positive potential via R4. However, when SCR1 is triggered and conducts, X is moved sharply negative. S1 is closed until the delayed off switching is wanted, so that C1 has no charge.

SCR2 controls the lamp. When S2 is closed, gate current is sufficient for SCR2 to conduct, so the lamp remains lit. When S2 is moved to the off position, gate current is no longer available for SCR2 through R4, but SCR2 continues to conduct in the normal way.

S1 is the second pole of this switch, so opens with S2. C1 charges until SCR1 conducts as explained. Y of C2 is negative as SCR2 is conducting, and when side X of this capacitor abruptly moves negative Y momentarily carries the anode of SCR2 down and stops SCR2 conducting. Conduction is not resumed as S2 is open.

The lamp thus remains lit for some 15 to 30 seconds (or as arranged) after operating S1/2. One use for such a device is to give illumination on an outdoor path, as example, without having to return to switch off, and without any need for lengthy wiring.

With these circuits, a relay will allow easy control of mains voltage lamps.

UJT Delay On or Delay Off

SCRs remain in the on condition when triggered, but it is possible to arrange the circuit so that this is reversed, and an off

74

switching action is obtained as described. The circuit in Figure 43 A will provide an "on" switching action for process timing etc. where a bulb is to light when the interval has passed. A uni-junction transistor is used. Alternatively, by adding the second part of the circuit B, an off action can be obtained.

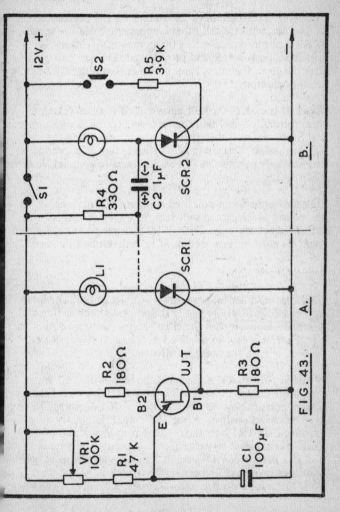

FIG. 43.

The timer consists of C1, charging through VR1 and R1. Values here give an interval of about 15 seconds upwards, but can be modified in the way described. When the UJT conducts, gate current triggers SCR1, so that indicator lamp L1 lights. This is the whole circuit for a delayed on indication, and a switch would be placed in one supply lead (e.g. S1).

For delayed off switching, L1 is removed and R4 connected in its place, with C2 and other components added as shown. SCR2 is put into conduction by momentarily closing S2, which is a push switch and provides gate current through R5. This results in the relay, lamp, or other device in SCR2 anode circuit operating.

When S1 is closed, the UJT delay circuit receives current, and eventually SCR1 will conduct. As SCR2 was conducting, but SCR1 was not, the charge on the commutating capacitor C2 is as shown. Triggering SCR1 thus swings SCR2 anode momentarily negative and so SCR2 ceases to conduct, as in Figure 42.

C2 needs to be a non-polarised component, or reversible, and the power which can be switched off by this means is influenced by its value. With SCR2 operating a low resistance load, C2 must be increased or SCR2 will not be turned off.

1 to 5 Minute Timer

This interval timer incorporates a Schmitt trigger. The interval covered is generally handy for processes such as film and print development, and the circuit can be incorporated in an egg timer. It is easy to modify values so that the device can be used outside the range mentioned.

When S1 (Figure 44) is placed in the on position, C1 commences to charge through VR1 and R2. TR1 base is held at a steady potential by R3, R4 and TR2. As C1 charges, TR1 emitter moves positive. When TR1 emitter is slightly more positive than TR1 base the negative base bias of this PNP transistor causes it to pass collector current. This supplies bias for TR2 base. When TR2 conducts the voltage drop across R4 increases, moving TR1 base further negative. At the same time the voltage drop across VR2 rises, moving the base of

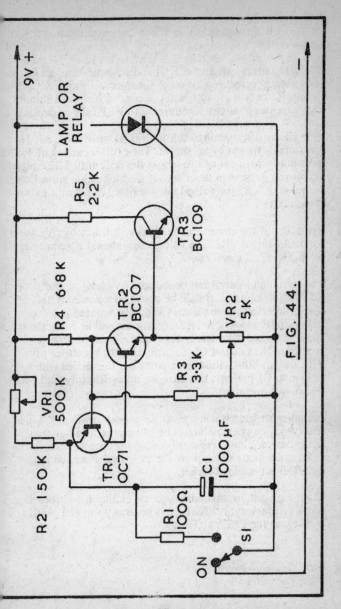

FIG. 44.

9V +

LAMP OR RELAY

R5 2·2 K

TR3 BC109

R4 6·8 K

TR2 BC107

VR1 500 K

R2 150 K

TR1 OC71

VR2 5K

R3 3·3 K

C1 1000 μF

R1 100 Ω

S1

ON

77

TR3 positive, so that this NPN transistor supplies gate current for the SCR through R5. The SCR is triggered, lighting the lamp.

When the unit is switched off, C1 is discharged through R1, so as to obtain correct repetition of the interval. With VR1 out of circuit, R2 only is present, and the interval is about 1 minute. This increases to about 5 minutes with VR1 fully in circuit.

VR2 allows adjustment to suit individual transistors, and 1k was suitable for the types shown. The emitter current of TR3 must not be high enough to trigger the SCR until TR2 emitter has moved positive as described. If the bulb lights immediately, the value of VR2 (or a fixed resistor fitted as substitute) must be reduced.

Operation of the circuit can be checked initially by clipping a voltmeter across VR2. The voltage here should rise abruptly when TR1/TR2 conduct.

The minimum interval can be reduced by changing the value of R2. With 47k here, it should be about 20 seconds. If only shorter intervals are required, C1 may be reduced in value. With 470μF and 47k for R2, adjustment will lie from about 10 seconds to 2 minutes. Longer intervals can be arranged by increasing the value of C1, or increasing the resistance of VR1, R2, or both. However, a point can be reached where leakage in C1 prevents this charging up sufficiently, and TR1 is then not operated.

An indicator lamp is convenient for processes where it will be observed. Elsewhere, a buzzer or bell can be fitted instead. With these, a parallel resistor is usually needed to hold on the SCR, and a diode to suppress the back emf generated in the coil. This is described earlier.

Other high gain, small audio type and similar transistors should prove satisfactory. A PNP type is necessary for TR1, with NPN types for TR2 and TR3.

Priority Indicator

In the section dealing with relays, a priority indicator was shown. Such a device can be used for two competitors playing "Snap" or in quiz games, to indicate who was first to press a button, this avoiding any argument. Two SCRs can be used in a similar type of circuit. The electronic operation is instantaneous and an actual tie is virtually impossible.

In Figure 45 indicator lamp L1 is controlled by SCR1. This competitor has the push switch PB1, which he must press immediately on seeing similar cards, or when prepared to reply to a question. In a similar way, indicator lamp L2 is controlled by SCR2, which has push switch PB2 for the second competitor.

With both switches open, the lamps are not lit, so the anode of each SCR is at full positive potential. If PB1 is pressed, current is taken through L2 and R2, to SCR1 gate, triggering the SCR so that it conducts. This lights L1, showing that PB1 was operated. If PB2 is now closed, current for SCR2 gate is via R1,

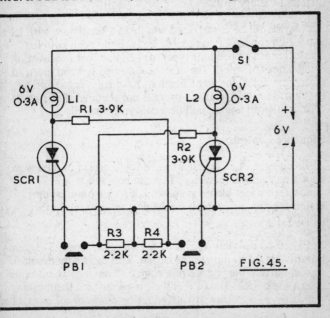

FIG. 45.

but the anode of SCR1 has moved negative, as SCR1 is conducting. As a result, there is insufficient gate current to trigger SCR2, so that pressing PB2 cannot light L2.

Should PB2 be operated first, the situation is of course reversed. R2 cannot supply enough gate current for SCR1, and L1 does not light. Once the circuit is operated, either lamp stays lit until S1 is opened, which restores the original neutral conditions.

R3 and R4 are not essential with some SCRs. However, a sensitive SCR can be triggered even with the opposing lamp lit, if these resistors are not present. If preferred, this may be overcome by increasing the values of R1 and R2, but it may be found that these have to be of dissimilar resistance, even with two SCRs of apparently the same type. There is in any case no need to use the exact values shown for R1 to R4, provided it is not possible to trigger SCR2 after L1 is lit, or SCR1 when L2 is lit. The circuit can also be arranged to work satisfactorily with lamps of other than 6V or 6.3V 0.3A type, or with a different battery voltage.

The device can be constructed wholly in a small box, with L1 and L2 on top, and two flexible leads to the push switches. The latter can be pendant types, or bell switches mounted on small blocks of wood. They can be coloured red and green to match the bulbs, for identification. As current is only drawn for short intervals, a large battery is not required. Four 1½V cells, in a 4-cell holder, will be a convenient supply.

Sequence Control

A silicon controlled rectifier can be used instead of a relay to start a mechanical sequence. This can be a single sweep of windscreen wiper blades as shown later, or a more complex action for process control, mechanical vending, and other activity.

In Figure 46 contacts S1 and S2 are normally open. S1 is temporarily closed to initiate the action. This can be by means of a push-button, the passage of a coin, or from a mechanical or electronic switch. The SCR is then triggered and the motor runs, driving the disc through reduction worm or other gearing.

Motion of the disc closes contacts S2, switching off the SCR. Rotation continues until the depression in the disc allows contacts S2 to open.

R1 is to limit gate current, and such a mechanism can be arranged to run from a wide range of voltages. Rotation of the motor performs the required sequence of operations.

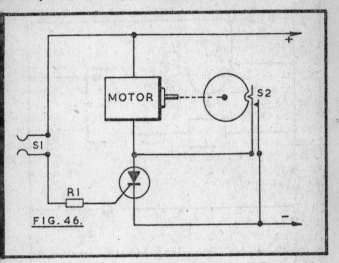

FIG. 46.

Wiper Delay

The continuous operation of a vehicle windscreen wiper is not necessary during very fine rain. It is something of a nuisance, and can scratch the windscreen if grit is present without enough water. To avoid switching the wiper on and off at regular intervals, a wiper delay can be added. This is a separate unit, needing only to be connected across one of the existing switches, or from motor to chassis. It enables the wiper blade to give one sweep, then return to rest, at a periodic interval which can be adjusted to suit conditions.

Figure 47 is a circuit of this unit. It is connected into the vehicle wiring at points X-X. S1 is the switch controlling the delay unit, and will normally be in the off position. S2 is the usual vehicle wiper switch, which will be open except when normal continuous operation of the wiper is required. S3 is an automatic switch which is incorporated in the wiper mechanism. Its purpose is to complete the circuit when S2 is open, unless the wipers are in the parked position. Without S3, the

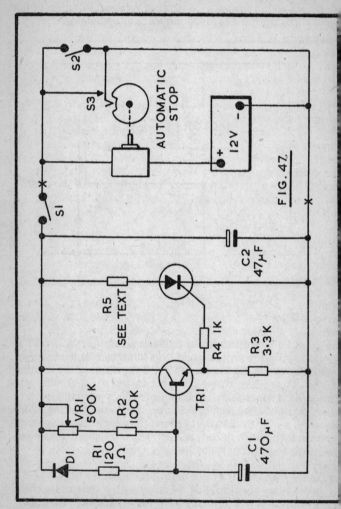

FIG. 47.

ipers would come to rest at any position on the screen, epending on when S2 was opened. This is avoided as S3 maintains the circuit until the mechanical device allows the contacts ɔ open.

Assuming that delayed operation is wanted, S1 is closed. S3 is open because the wipers are parked. Approximately 12V will now be available for the delay unit, the positive circuit being through the motor. A small current will flow through VR1 and R2, so that capacitor C1 begins to charge. The peed with which C1 charges depends on the setting of VR1.

When TR1 begins to conduct due to the rise in base voltage, current to trigger the SCR becomes available through R4. With the SCR conducting, current for the motor is available through R5 and S1, so that the motor begins to run. This motion closes S3, which will keep the motor running until the wipers have returned to the parking position. While S3 is closed, it shorts the positive/negative supply lines of the delay unit so that the SCR is turned off, and C1 is discharged through R1 and D1.

After the full movement of the wiper S3 opens, so the 12V supply via the motor is again available for the delay unit, and C1 starts to charge. This is repeated so long as S1 is closed.

With the component values shown, a delay of up to about 45 seconds should be obtained, though this depends somewhat on individual components. Generally a delay of about 10-20 seconds will be wanted. It is possible to change the values of VR1, R2, or C1, if wished, to alter the delay. C2 is to suppress transients which may come from the supply line.

The running current of the usual motor is not particularly heavy, but there is a high current surge at the moment of switching on. To avoid the use of a very large SCR, current is limited by R5. With a large SCR and R5 of minimum value, the motor can start at almost usual power. However, slower running until contacts S3 close is of very little practical disadvantage, and allows R5 to be higher in value, and the SCR to have a lower current rating. Provided the motor always starts reliably so that the automatic mechanism can close S3, much less than full power need be available, and this greatly eases conditions for the SCR.

Tests made with this circuit showed that the maximum resistance at R5 which permitted reliable starting was 3 ohms. With a 3 ohm resistor here, and assuming the motor at rest to have virtually zero resistance, the surge when switching on is limited to 4A. Normal running current for this wiper (full voltage) was 2A. However, it will be realised that other wiper motors could have different ratings. So if starting proved to be too sluggish, R5 would have to be reduced in value, and the SCR rating increased if necessary.

As shown, the circuit has to be connected to motor and chassis, or in parallel with S2 or S3. It is likely that the S2 connections at the motor will be most readily identified, and provide the most convenient connecting point. As S3 is incorporated in the motor unit in most cases a connector for leads to S2 will be present here.

In the event of switching not being as shown, and positive chassis, connections for the unit would have to be modified to suit.

Vehicle Protector

The purpose of this unit is to dissuade an intending car thief, as it can call attention to his activities by sounding the vehicle horn. This warning may sound even if an unauthorised person only opens a door momentarily with a view to removing some object inside, and will in any case be given if anyone gets behind the driving wheel in the usual way without immobilising the circuit.

The protective device, Figure 48, can be divided into sections, SCR1 with R5 can be considered first. The SCR anode is able to receive current from point B, but SCR1 is normally not conducting, so that no voltage is present for the transistors. When the positive circuit to point A is completed, even if only momentarily, SCR1 is triggered, and remains on.

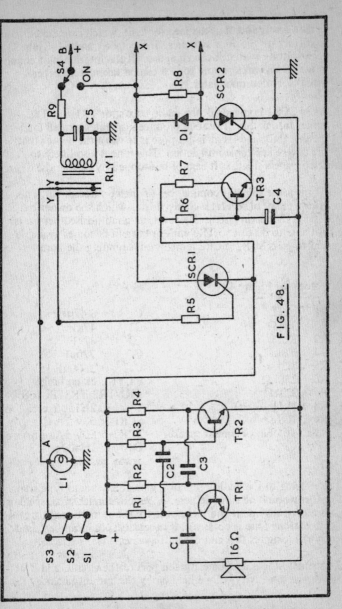

FIG. 48.

85

Polarity is arranged for vehicles with negative chassis. Point A is then easily found at the interior light, which is operated automatically by the door switches. These are S1 and S2, while S3 is the fitting switch for manual use. (If the interior light circuit is not as shown, a supply for R5 can be taken from other circuits, as described later.)

When SCR1 is triggered, the audio oscillator TR1 and TR2 comes into action. The tone produced operates a small loudspeaker unit, and its main purpose is to warn the owner that the device has come into action. This tone is also likely to discourage a thief, as it cannot be stopped by closing the door.

At the same time C4 commences to charge through R6. This gives a delay of several seconds, during which the owner can disable the alarm circuit. However, an unauthorised person is not able to do this so TR3 emitter current becomes available, and triggers SCR2. SCR2 remains on, sounding the horn.

Values for Figure 48

R1	1kΩ	C1	0.47μF
R2	33kΩ	C2	47nF
R3	22kΩ	C3	47nF
R4	6.8kΩ	C4	220μF 15V
R5	2.2kΩ	C5	3500μF 15V
R6	220kΩ	RLY1	2k coil relay
R7	2.2kΩ	TR1/TR2/TR3	BC108,
R8	1kΩ		2N1306, etc.
R9	100 Ω	SCR1	50V 1A
Small 16 ohm or similar speaker		SCR2	50V 3A or 5A
		D1	1N4001
		2-way switch	

Referring to the audio oscillator, almost any audio type transistors whould be suitable here. A 2½in or similar small speaker is most convenient and its impedance is not important, provided a strong tone is obtained. If necessary, pitch can be raised by reducing resistor and capacitor values.

A small SCR is adequate for this part of the circuit, and if of average sensitivity will be held on by the current taken by

TR1/2. Should this SCR revert to the off position when the supply to R5 is broken, an additional steady load can be provided for it, by means of a 1k resistor from positive to negative lines of the oscillator.

The delay provided by TR3 depends somewhat on the sensitivity of SCR2, and should be found to be around 5 to 6 seconds, with the values given. The interval can be increased by having higher values for R6 and C4, or can be reduced by fitting smaller values here. A thief, of course, has no idea what is happening when the audio tone commences, but it is only necessary that the sounding of the horn is delayed briefly.

The legitimate user is warned by the tone that the circuit is in action, so opens S4, thus switching off SCR1 and preventing SCR2 operating. The position of S4 is known only to the user, and it should be within easy reach. A thief has only a few seconds in which to immobilise the device with S4, even if he should try to locate it.

Connecting points are most easily located by referring to the vehicle circuit. It should be possible to run a thin insulated lead quite inconspicuously from the interior light. An older vehicle might have space between door and frame for a push-switch to be fitted. This normally occupies a hole at the hinged side, and is depressed by the door. A switch which closes when released is necessary.

Supply point B has to be a point where voltage is always available. This will be found at the fuseways for accessories which are not controlled by the ignition key (as example, parking lights).

Where the circuits are not known, a test with a voltmeter will quickly show points where the accumulator supply is available, with meter negative returned to chassis.

Points X-X are wired to the warning device. This can be the vehicle horn where SCR2 will come in parallel with the horn switch circuit. In other cases it is necessary to connect SCR2 anode to positive, so that leads can be taken from the cathode and chassis. Tests with a meter will show how the circuit should be connected. Failing this, it would be possible to use a relay so that the circuits are isolated; or a completely separate warning device (loud bell or horn). D1 is to protect SCR2, and R8 to provide a holding-on current, as described elsewhere.

The remaining part of the circuit allows the user to leave the vehicle without triggering SCR1. When S4 has been put in the off position, C5 has charged through R9 and so contacts Y-Y of the relay are held open. This interrupts the circuit at A. After moving S4 to the position which places the alarm in action, contacts Y-Y remain open about 15 seconds, so that the operation of S1 or S2 to leave the vehicle cannot trigger SCR1.

The overall circuit can be simplified if wished, with some loss of protection, though still remaining useful. If SCR1, relay, C5, R5 and R9 are omitted, current may be drawn directly from point A. The circuit can then be immobilised by operating S4 before the interval provided by R6 and C4 has elapsed, or by closing the door so that S1 or S2 opens again. A delay circuit to permit leaving the vehicle is then not necessary provided the door is closed within the interval allowed by R6/C4.

Automatic Battery Charger

Figure 49 is the circuit of an accumulator charger in which the charging current is controlled by the battery voltage, falling as voltage rises. Such a charger gives maximum charge when the battery is in poor condition, the rate falling as charging nears completion. Eventually current drops to a trickle charge to keep the accumulator in condition.

The mains transformer, full-wave rectifier, and SCR1 are rated for the maximum current and voltage wanted. For 12V charging, a 17V secondary is suitable, though other voltages are seen, and a rating of 3A to 5A is generally easily adequate for home use.

During maximum charging, current through R1 and D1 triggers SCR1 so that the full rate is available. The voltage across VR1 and R3 is relatively low, so that D2 does not conduct and SCR2 is off. The level at which D2 conducts, relative to the accumulator voltage, depends on the setting of VR1.

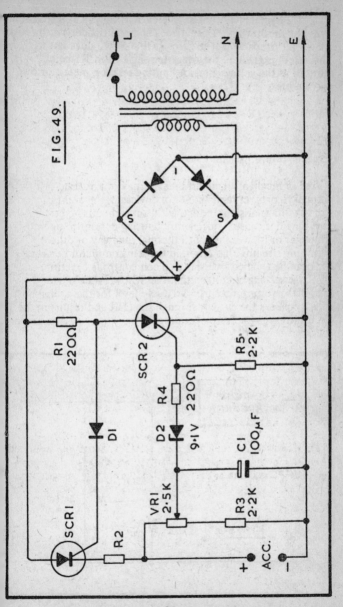

FIG. 49.

89

When D2 commences to pass gate current to SCR2, this SCR switches on, moving D1 negative. The potential derived through R1 for D1 drops almost to zero, so that SCR1 does not trigger. This effect is gradual, the triggering angle of SCR1 being reduced as the voltage rises. A limiting resistor, meter, or fuse may be present at R2.

Excess Voltage Breaker

A fuse or mechanical circuit breaker may not operate fast enough to protect semiconductor devices in the event of an excess voltage arising. In fact, with some circuits, excess voltage may not cause a sufficiently unusual current to operate a breaker or blow a fuse until thermal runaway or other damaging situation has arisen in the semiconductor devices. This can be avoided by using a silicon controlled rectifier and a voltage sensing circuit, so that the SCR provides a heavy load if the voltage rises beyond a safe level for the equipment. This by-passes the current through the SCR and results in the circuit breaker (or fuse) operating.

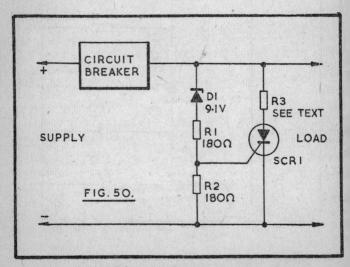

FIG. 50.

A circuit of this type designed for approximately 9V is shown in Figure 50. With the normal voltage present, D1 does not conduct, so the SCR receives no gate current and imposes no load on the circuit. When the supply rises beyond the zener voltage, D1 conducts, and gate current through R1 triggers the SCR. The latter conducts, the load across the circuit depending largely on R3. If the circuit breaker (or fuse) operates at 2A, R3 can be about 4.7 ohm. The purpose of R3 is to limit the short circuit current to a level which is not too great for the SCR fitted. Should circuit requirements make a larger current necessary, R3 must be reduced, and a larger SCR fitted, so that R3 and the SCR in series always operate the circuit breaker. Alternatively, for smaller currents of say under 1A, R3 can be increased in value and a 1A SCR may be used.

R1 and R2 limit the current through D1 (which is a 400mW zener here). Currents through D1, R1, R2 and the SCR are momentary, as voltage is removed by the breaker

Current ratings can be scaled up or down as described. The operating voltage can also be modified by changing D1, or by using a potential divider as its supply. A variable potentiometer will give an adjustable over-voltage setting.

If a suitable fuse or circuit breaker is incorporated, this circuit will afford protection for equipment operated from various power sources, or from a variable supply where the fact that the voltage has been adjusted may be overlooked. It is convenient as an add-on circuit for an existing circuit breaker, which may not protect equipment incorporating semiconductor devices.

Dimmer/Heat Control

The simple circuit in Figure 51 operates directly from 200/250V AC mains, and will reduce and control the power supplied to relatively low wattage loads. It is thus suitable for dimming a 40W or similar filament lamp, or reducing the heat of a soldering iron which is kept switched on for some length of time. It is not intended for inductive loads, or fluorescent lamps.

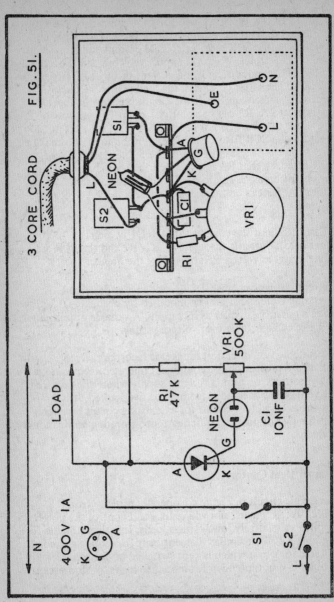

FIG. 51.

3 CORE CORD

92

In this circuit, triggering of the SCR is controlled by the neon, which provides gate current. The voltage reaching the neon each cycle depends on the setting of VR1, so by this means the conduction angle is changed. Conduction is maximum with VR1 slider at R1. With VR1 slider fully in the other direction, the SCR is held off completely.

The circuit cannot provide completely full power or brilliance at the maximum setting of VR1. If this is required, a switch S1 is necessary to remove the SCR from the circuit. It is convenient to use a potentiometer with switch for VR1, so that switch S2 opens when VR1 is at minimum power, unless other means of on-off switching are provided.

A 400V 1A SCR with wire leads is easily adequate here. Its full rating will frequently require the use of a clip-on heat sink for it. If the load is in the region of 100W or more, unplug from the mains after a period of use, and check if the SCR feels hot. If noticeably so, a finned sink would be wise. This simply pushes on, as with similar transistors.

The neon can be one of the small, wire-ended types used as indicators. These are generally operated with a series resistor of about 220k, when used directly from 200/250V AC mains. They are available as replacements for soldering irons, etc. The same type, but with MES or MBC fitting, is equally suitable. If a fitting with series resistor should be obtained, the resistor is removed.

Values for R1 and VR1 need not be exactly as shown. C1 should be of adequate rating — say 350V to 500V.

Safety

House power is supplied by live (L) and neutral (N) circuits. Neutral is normally earthed, or at low voltage relative to earth. The other conductor (L) is at high voltage relative to earth, and contact with it, or any circuits or items common to it, can cause electric shock.

To avoid this, a circuit such as that in Figure 51 must be wired and built so as to provide complete safety. All components must be enclosed in an adequately insulated box, and construction is so arranged that no bare leads, live fixing screws, or other circuits can be touched. The fixing nut of VR1 should be covered by an insulated knob, and if the shaft is metal, the screw hole of the knob should be filled with sealing wax or other similar material.

Where a lamp is controlled by such a device (which itself forms a type of off switch) the switch should be in the L conductor. Thus if S2 is open, or the SCR is not conducting, the lamp itself is common to the neutral only. Where a single pole switch or similar device is placed in the N conductor, the lamp would remain at high voltage relative to earth, even when off. This could present a shock hazard.

Where a circuit receives power from a reversible 2-pin plug, as may be the case with a table lamp, as example, L and N conductors will not be known, and will in any case depend on which way the plug is inserted. This also applies to the use of lampholder adapters.

If a soldering iron is used, or other item with earth, a 3-core cord will be present, and a 3-pin plug should be used as in Figure 51. Here, the soldering iron outlet is fitted to an insulated box, which incorporates the SCR controller. This allows the correct Live, Neutral and Earth connections to be retained. N and L sockets are here shown as if looking at the fitting from behind, and they will be found marked by the sockets. The iron is plugged in here, and a plug fitted to the 3-core cord from the box allows the device to be operated from any ordinary outlet.

Similar points will apply to other mains-operated circuits. For safety, reliable earthing must be present for all items which have an earth connection. It is also necessary to distinguish correctly between L and N conductors. Construction of such devices may be in a strong, adequately insulated box, such as those available for mains junctions; or it may be in a metal box, which must be earthed through the 3-core cord and earth pin of the plug. (Other, alternative earths must not be used.)

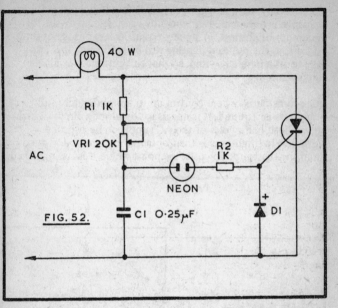

Figure 52 is another half-wave dimmer control circuit. Component values need not be exactly as shown, but will be found to be satisfactory for typical applications. Diode D1 limits the negative gate voltage, to prevent gate avalanche.

The limitation of half-wave circuits arises because even with the angle of conduction of the SCR at maximum, only half-wave current can be supplied to the load. This limits the power available. Such circuits also produce noticeable flicker, at some power settings. Despite this, they have practical uses, and also offer an easy means of reducing the temperature of small power devices such as a soldering iron.

For greater control so that about full brilliance or power can be obtained, a full-wave circuit is necessary.

Full-Wave Dimmer

With the half-wave dimmer circuit conduction is obtained in only one direction, or with alternative half-cycles of the AC mains supply. As a result, a fairly substantial reduction in brilliance is obtained, even with the variable control set for maximum brightness. In some circumstances, this is not important, as the reduced lighting will be sufficient. It is also easy to fit a parallel switch, so that full current is available when wanted.

In circumstances where control up to approximately full brightness is required, it is necessary to adopt a circuit which allows both half-cycles of the AC supply to be adjusted. Variation in brightness is then obtained from virtually maximum for the lamp, down to the point where it is extinguished.

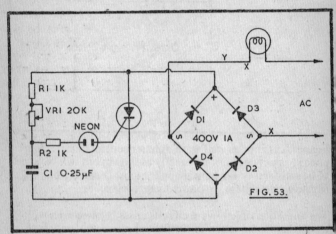

FIG. 53.

Figure 53 is a full-wave circuit which requires only the single SCR and four inexpensive diodes (or equivalent bridge rectifier). For one half cycle, conventional current flow is through D1, the SCR, and D2; during the next half cycle, flow is through D3, the SCR, and D4. It will be seen that current passes through the SCR in the same direction, for both half cycles. With the SCR fully conducting, it and the four diodes represent only a low series resistance for the lamp or other load.

Four 1N4004 or other 400V 1A rectifiers are suitable, with a 400V 1A SCR. These ratings will be satisfactory for loads up to 100W, with a safety factor. For heavier loads the device ratings can be increased to suit.

The neon is as described for the half-wave circuit. Very little additional building space will be required. It is essential that assembly is arranged so that there is no shock danger for the user, as explained earlier.

Radio Interference

It is sometimes found that various forms of SCR control of mains equipment will generate interference apparent with TV and radio receivers. Interference from this source will be present only when the device is in use.

Various methods may be employed to reduce and eliminate this trouble. A by-pass or suppressor capacitor will often be of aid. This would be from X to X in Figure 53. It can be about $0.05\mu F$. With a circuit having an earth, such capacitors may be used from neutral to earth and line to earth, the latter probably being most useful. A further capacitor can also be taken from N to L.

A suppressor choke may sometimes be added. This could be placed at Y in Figure 53 and would be about 2.5mH, and rated for the maximum current to be carried.

Chances of interference are reduced by using a metal box, as this can be earthed and then forms an earthing point for the suppressor capacitors. Metal boxes with knock out sections, as used for house wiring and similar purposes, are available in various sizes.

Occasionally the position of the device containing the SCR, or its location relative to aerial lead-in or other wiring, may contribute to the interference, so it may be worthwhile trying the unit elsewhere. If direct radiation is causing interference, it is helpful to keep the device away from receivers or other equipment.

TRIACs

Triacs

The SCR has anode, cathode and gate, and the anode and cathode polarity has to be observed as shown in various circuits. The SCR can conduct only during one half cycle of the wave (though the effects of full-wave control can be achieved by a circuit such as that in Figure 53). Instead of anode and cathode, the triac has two main terminals, in addition to the gate, and it can operate with either polarity. It will trigger on both halves of the cycle.

A triac thus allows virtually full power to be applied to a lamp, motor, or other controlled load, when operated with alternating current supplies. A typical 400V 6A triac will need about 25mA at 2.5V to trigger the gate, and the peak gate dissipation is some 10W to 20W according to type. The main terminals may be marked Anode 1 and Anode 2, or A1 and A2, or merely 1 and 2; or Mt1 and Mt2. Casing resembles that for SCRs of somewhat similar power rating.

Diacs

Diacs are sometimes used in conjunction with triacs, and are bi-directional trigger diodes. A typical diac can have a breakover rating of 28V to 36V in either direction. A diac may be used to provide a trigger pulse for the gate of a triac.

Drill or Motor Controller

Figure 54 shows the use of a triac for controlling the speed of an electric drill or similar motor, or for heat control, or dimming filament lamps. Values shown are for a 400V 6A triac and 350W or similar motor, but may of course be used with other loads. VR1 can generally be 50k to 200k. Low values here give insufficient control, as power cannot be fully reduced. Unnecessarily high values make the control abrupt. If the circuit is to be used with some particular load, VR1 can be chosen to suit.

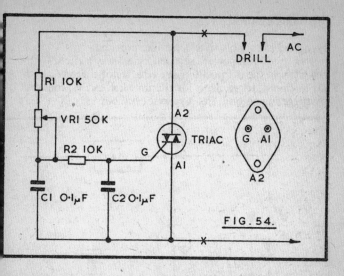

FIG. 54.

For small loads, or intermittent loads such as drilling, the triac needs no heat sink. But for lengthy periods of use at near maximum rating a heat sink is necessary. Note that this must be insulated from other items. It is obviously essential to un-plug the device from the mains before checking the triac temperature, which should not feel more than quite hot (75°C). If very hot, heat-sinking should be improved, or more ventila-tion should be allowed, or the load should be reduced.

A device of this kind should be constructed as described for the mains SCR controller, with properly wired plug and outlet to take the motor plug. Reference should be made to the safety points explained.

Similar points also arise regarding interference. A typical interference suppressor for this circuit would be to fit a 22 ohm resistor and 0.022μF capacitor in series from X to X. Or a 0.05μF capacitor here may suffice. Alternatively, a choke may be fitted between X and A2. It can have about 150 to 200 turns of 18swg wire, pile wound on a ½in diameter former. Capacitors should be for 350V AC or 750-1000V DC.

3-Position Control

Figure 55 is a simple triac controller providing "off", "half power" and "full power" selected by a 3-way switch. With the latter in the off position, the triac is not triggered. With D1 in circuit, triggering is for alternate half-cycles, followed by triggering on both half cycles for full power.

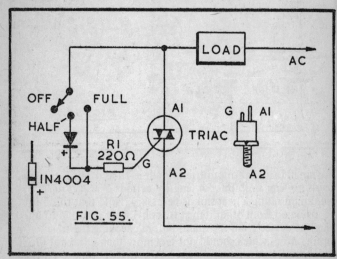

FIG. 55.

This circuit is useful for soldering irons, small heaters, etc. within the rating of the triac. It may be used for filament lamp control where the flickering effect of half-cycle operation is not important.

Low Voltage AC Motor Controller

Figure 56 shows a circuit which may be used to control the speed of a low voltage AC motor. Such a motor will have wound field and armature, and for models and similar purposes will generally be intended to run from about 6V to 24V.

Transformer T1 reduces the voltage of the AC mains supply, and should provide a somewhat higher voltage than the usual running voltage of the motor. The current rating will depend

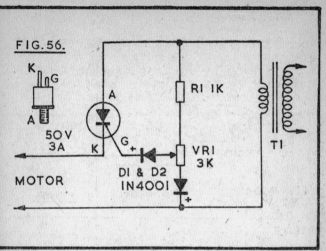

FIG. 56.

K G
A
50 V
3A
MOTOR

A
K G
D1 & D2
1N4001

R1 1K
VR1
3K

T1

on the motor, as will the current rating of the SCR. This is
shown as 3A, which will be sufficient for small motors not
drawing a current in excess of this figure. For larger motors
the rating will have to be increased to suit, and the SCR
should be attached to a heat sink or plate if operated at a
current found to increase its temperature appreciably.

T1 provides isolation from the mains circuit, but connections
should be arranged as described earlier, to avoid any possibil-
ity of mains voltages reaching a model or other equipment,
in the event of a fault developing.

Temperature Warning

The circuit in Figure 57 uses a VA1040 thermistor as a tem-
perature-sensing element, and operates a warning lamp when
the temperature falls below a point pre-set by VR1. The resistance of the thermistor rises as temperature falls — typical
figures are 450 ohm at 40°F, 750 ohm at 30°F, and 1200 ohm
at 10°F. At some particular resistance value, which depends on
the setting of VR1, the circuit is triggered. For a 6V supply, a
6.3V or 6V 0.3A or 0.5A indicator bulb is suitable. The circuit
can be arranged to operate with other thermistors, but some
component values may need modification.

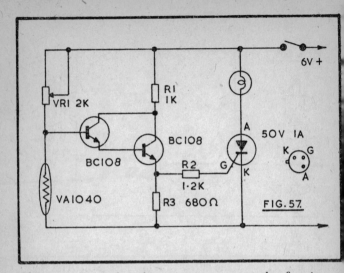

FIG. 57.

If set to operate when the temperature approaches freezing
point, the device will act as a frost warning. It may also be
used with livestock or plants as an indicator that heating
arrangements have failed or the temperature has fallen too
much. The thermistor can be at some distance from the device
but should be enclosed in a sealed tube or other small contain-
er, as if it becomes damp or wet this will tend to keep its
resistance low.

Notes

Notes

Please note overleaf is a list of other titles that are available in our range of Radio and Electronic Books.

These should be available from most good Booksellers, Radio Component Dealers and Mail Order Companies.

However, should you experience difficulty in obtaining any title in your area, then please write directly to the publishers enclosing payment to cover the cost of the book plus adequate postage.

BABANI PRESS & BERNARDS (PUBLISHERS) LTD
THE GRAMPIANS
SHEPHERDS BUSH ROAD
LONDON W6 7NF
ENGLAND

BP1	First Book of Transistor Equivalents and Substitutes	60p
BP2	Handbook of Radio, TV and Ind. & Transmitting Tube & Valve Equiv.	60p
BP6	Engineers and Machinists Reference Tables	50p
BP7	Radio and Electronic Colour Codes and Data Chart	25p
BP11	Practical Transistor Novelty Circuits	40p
BP14	Second Book of Transistor Equivalents	1.10p
BP22	79 Electronic Novelty Circuits	1.00p
BP23	First Book of Practical Electronic Projects	75p
BP24	52 Projects using IC741	95p
BP25	How to Build Your Own Electronic and Quartz Controlled Watches & Clocks	85p
BP26	Radio Antenna Handbook for Long Distance Reception & Transmission	85p
BP27	Giant Chart of Radio Electronic Semiconductor & Logic Symbols	60p
BP28	Resistor Selection Handbook (International Edition)	60p
BP29	Major Solid State Audio Hi-Fi Construction Projects	85p
BP30	Two Transistor Electronic Projects	85p
BP31	Practical Electical Re-wiring & Repairs	85p
BP32	How to Build Your Own Metal and Treasure Locators	1.00p
BP33	Electronic Calculator Users Handbook	95p
BP34	Practical Repair & Renovation of Colour TV's	1.25p
BP35	Handbook of IC Audio Preamplifier and Power Amplifier Construction	1.25p
BP36	50 Circuits Using Germanium, Silicon and Zener Diodes	75p
BP37	50 Projects Using Relays, SCR's and TRIAC's	1.25p
BP38	Fun & Games with your Electronic Calculator	75p
BP39	50 (FET) Field Effect Transistor Projects	1.25p
BP40	Digital IC Equivalents and Pin Connections	2.50p
BP41	Linear IC Equivalents and Pin Connections	2.75p
BP42	50 Simple L.E.D. Circuits	75p
BP43	How to make Walkie-Talkies	1.25p
BP44	IC 555 Projects	1.75p
BP45	Projects on Opto-Electronics	1.25p
BP46	Radio Circuits using IC's	1.35p
BP47	Mobile Discotheque Handbook	1.35p
BP48	Electronic Projects for Beginners	1.35p
BP49	Popular Electronic Projects	1.45p
BP50	IC LM3900 Projects	1.35p
BP51	Electronic Music and Creative Tape Recording	1.25p
BP52	Long Distance Television Reception (TV-DX) for the Enthusiast	1.45p
BP53	Practical Electronic Calculations and Formulae	2.25p
BP54	Your Electronic Calculator and Your Money	1.35p
BP55	Radio Stations Guide	1.45p
BP56	Electronic Security Devices	1.45p
BP57	How to Build your own Solid State Oscilloscope	1.50p
BP58	50 Circuits using 7400 Series IC's	1.35p
BP59	Second Book of CMOS IC Projects	1.50p
BP60	Practical Construction of Pre-Amps, Tone Controls, Filters and Attenuators	1.45p
BP61	Beginners Guide to Digital Techniques	95p
BP62	Elements of Electronics – Book 1	2.25p
BP63	Elements of Electronics – Book 2	2.25p
BP64	Elements of Electronics – Book 3	2.25p
BP65	Single IC Projects	1.50p
BP66	Beginners Guide to Microprocessors and Computing	N.Y.A.
BP67	Counter Driver and Numeral Display Projects	N.Y.A.
BP68	Choosing and Using Your Hi-Fi	N.Y.A.
BP69	Electronic Games	N.Y.A.
126	Boys Book of Crystal Sets	25p
160	Coil Design and Construction Manual	75p
196	AF–RF Reactance – Frequency Chart for Constructors	15p
200	Handbook of Practical Electronic Musical Novelties	50p
201	Practical Transistorised Novelties for Hi-Fi Enthusiasts	35p
202	Handbook of Integrated Circuits (IC's) Equivalents and Substitutes	1.00p
203	IC's and Transistor Gadgets Construction Handbook	60p
205	First Book of Hi-Fi Loudspeaker Enclosures	75p
207	Practical Electronic Science Projects	75p
208	Practical Stereo and Quadrophony Handbook	75p
210	The Complete Car Radio Manual	1.00p
211	First Book of Diode Characteristics Equivalents and Substitutes	1.25p
213	Electronic Circuits for Model Railways	1.00p
214	Audio Enthusiasts Handbook	85p
215	Shortwave Circuits and Gear for Experimenters and Radio Hams	85p
217	Solid State Power Supply Handbook	85p
218	Build Your Own Electronic Experimenters Laboratory	85p
219	Solid State Novelty Projects	85p
220	Build Your Own Solid State Hi-Fi and Audio Accessories	85p
221	28 Tested Transistor Projects	95p
222	Solid State Short Wave Receivers for Beginners	95p
223	50 Projects using IC CA3130	95p
224	50 CMOS IC Projects	95p
225	A Practical Introduction to Digital IC's	95p
226	How to Build Advanced Short Wave Receivers	1.20p
227	Beginners Guide to Building Electronic Projects	1.25p
228	Essential Theory for the Electronics Hobbyist	1.25p